Bruckmann & Co., from Rudolf Lesch

PORTRAIT OF A GIRL, by Auguste Renoir

Songs and Pictures

BY ROBERT FORESMAN

FIRST BOOK

AMERICAN BOOK COMPANY

NEW YORK CINCINNATI CHICAGO

BOSTON ATLANTA DALLAS SAN FRANCISCO

Copyright, 1937, by
AMERICAN BOOK COMPANY

All rights reserved

Foresman—Songs and Pictures

First Book

BASED ON
FORESMAN—FIRST BOOK OF SONGS

Copyright, 1925, by
AMERICAN BOOK COMPANY

W. P. 1

MADE IN U.S.A.

Foreword

THE FORESMAN *Books of Songs and Pictures* will find a place wherever music teaching aspires to acquaint its disciples with the finer things of song in their original simplicity and grandeur. These collections have a definite function, for in them the great musical heritage of the world is represented by songs which should be a part of the life and cultural background of all people. They are, moreover, carefully graded musically, and have a substantial underlying pedagogical *motif*.

The songs in the series have been chosen from two main sources—the work of the classical composers and the folk songs of all nations. The aim has been to assemble a group of songs which have stood the test of time, which mirror the characteristics and musical contributions of many national cultures, and which are universal in appeal. To these have been added a number of songs by contemporary composers, which serve as a connecting link with the child's out-of-school musical experience. To aid the teacher in making use of this wealth of material, a *topical index* has been supplied, in which the songs are listed under headings for easy reference.

The progression represented in the arrangement of this material is on a basis of *feeling subtlety*. In the early songs, the formal and structural element of various phases of repetition is used for a double reason: first, because such songs are easy to learn and quickly assume permanence in memory; second, because the germ theme in them, as found in the first phrase or motive, is obvious, and may easily be made the real basis in studying the song. As the work progresses, the same principle of repetition and theme dominance continues, with an increasing variety and complexity in the structure of the songs.

The pictures in the series represent the great art heritage of the world which, like music, should help form a cultural background for the boys and girls in our schools. Since early familiarity with a variety of masterpieces is a partial basis for art appreciation, the works of both contemporary artists and masters of the past have been reproduced. Such subjects have been selected as are of interest to boys and girls and at the same time lend themselves, with the songs, to integrated courses of study.

ACKNOWLEDGMENTS. The author wishes to express his grateful appreciation of the assistance rendered by the many persons whose services have been enlisted in various phases of the work and in criticism and suggestion. Especial acknowledgment is due to Miss Laura Bryant, Director of Music in the Public Schools of Ithaca, New York; to Mr. Robert A. Coan; and to Mr. Mayhew L. Lake, who has written many of these harmonizations and accompaniments and whose musical judgments have been of the greatest value.

The music of "Morning Song," by Arthur Edward Johnstone, and of "The Weather Vane," is used by permission of Carl Fischer, Inc., owners of the copyright, to whom acknowledgment of their courtesy is hereby made.

PICTURES

PORTRAIT OF A GIRL	Auguste Renoir	frontispiece
FAIRIES' COURT	Lee Woodward	facing 24
THE MILL AT WYK	Jacob Ruisdael	facing 40
THE MOTHER	Pieter de Hooch	facing 69
THE SINGING BOYS	Franz Hals	facing 86
THE BOY COLUMBUS	John Whiting	facing 116

THE FAIRY PIPER

7

Sigmund Spaeth

Melody by Mendelssohn

A PRAYER

Adapted from George Herbert
Melody by Mozart

Reverently

1. May we learn, O Lord of love,
2. So shall ev-'ry act ap-pear

Thy dear hand in all to see;
Wor-thy of Thy fair de-sign;

Bend-ing to our dai-ly task,
Sim-plest ser-vice, done for Thee,

May we do it all for Thee.
Makes each com-mon deed di-vine.

EVENING SONG

Folk Song

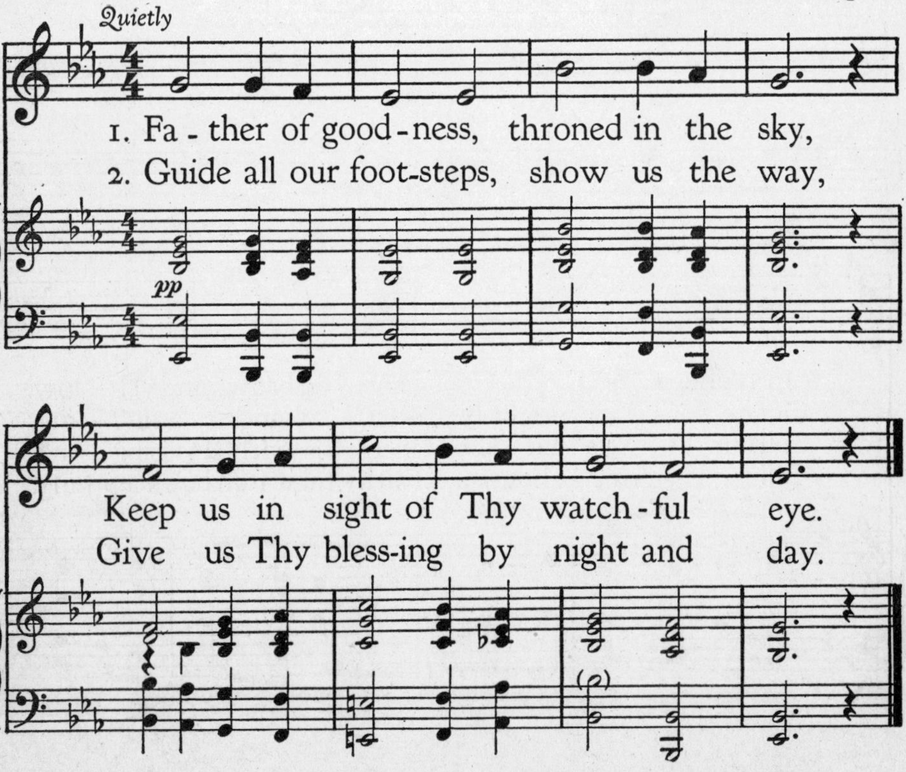

Quietly

1. Fa-ther of good-ness, throned in the sky,
2. Guide all our foot-steps, show us the way,

Keep us in sight of Thy watch-ful eye.
Give us Thy bless-ing by night and day.

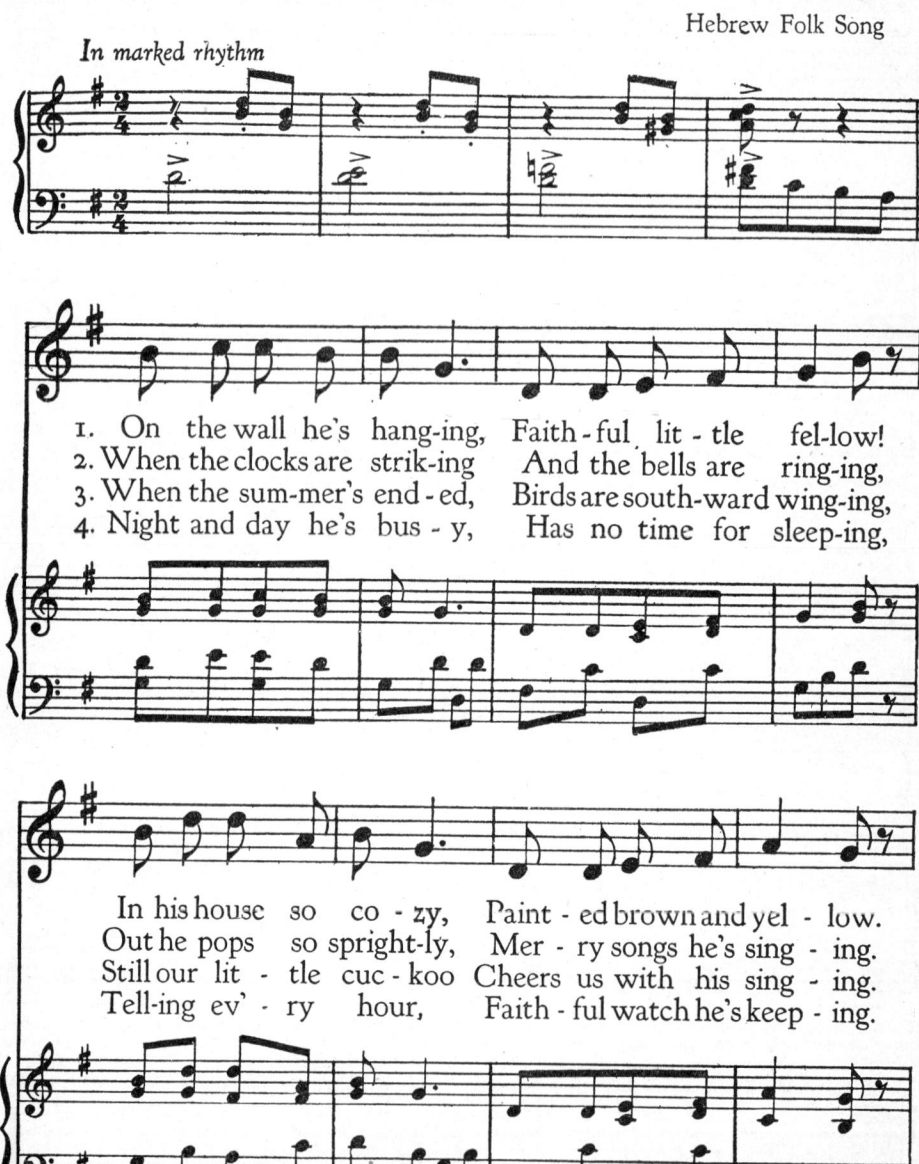

He knows I love to play
He brings the sum-mer rain

And run with him all day,
To splash the win-dow-pane,

And so he comes and calls me
And then he sends the sun-beams

To join him on his way.
To make it shine a-gain.

As he sat and car-oled from the tree.
But that song still ech-oes soft and clear.

A-DANCING

Cecil Cowdrey Slovene Folk Song

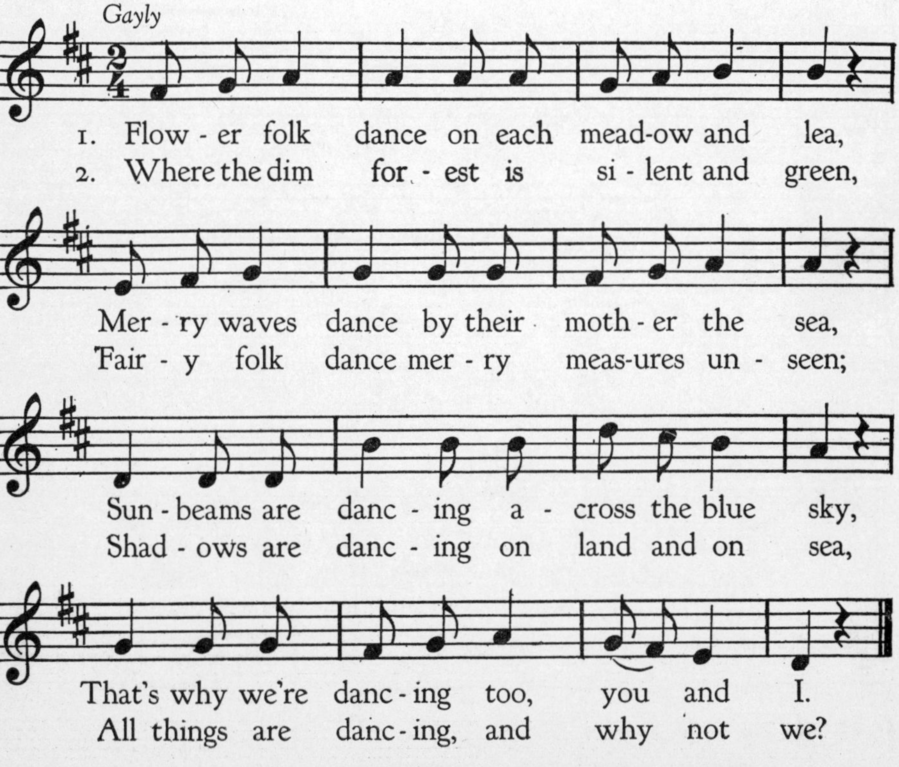

Gayly

1. Flow-er folk dance on each mead-ow and lea,
2. Where the dim for-est is si-lent and green,

Mer-ry waves dance by their moth-er the sea,
Fair-y folk dance mer-ry meas-ures un-seen;

Sun-beams are danc-ing a-cross the blue sky,
Shad-ows are danc-ing on land and on sea,

That's why we're danc-ing too, you and I.
All things are danc-ing, and why not we?

THE MERRY-GO-ROUND

Cecil Cowdrey

Melody by Schumann
Used in "Papillons"

1. Who'll go for a ride on the mer-ry-go-round?
2. In haste, one and all to the sad-dles we climb;

Come, mount in a hur-ry! I hear the bell sound!
We're up in a mo-ment, and seat-ed in time.

Gay sad-dles are wait-ing! Who trav-els to-day?
The sig-nal is giv-en. The ground far be-low,

Come one, and come all, we shall soon ride a-way!
Now slow-ly, now fast-er and fast-er we go!

SONG OF THE SEASONS

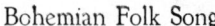

Bohemian Folk Song

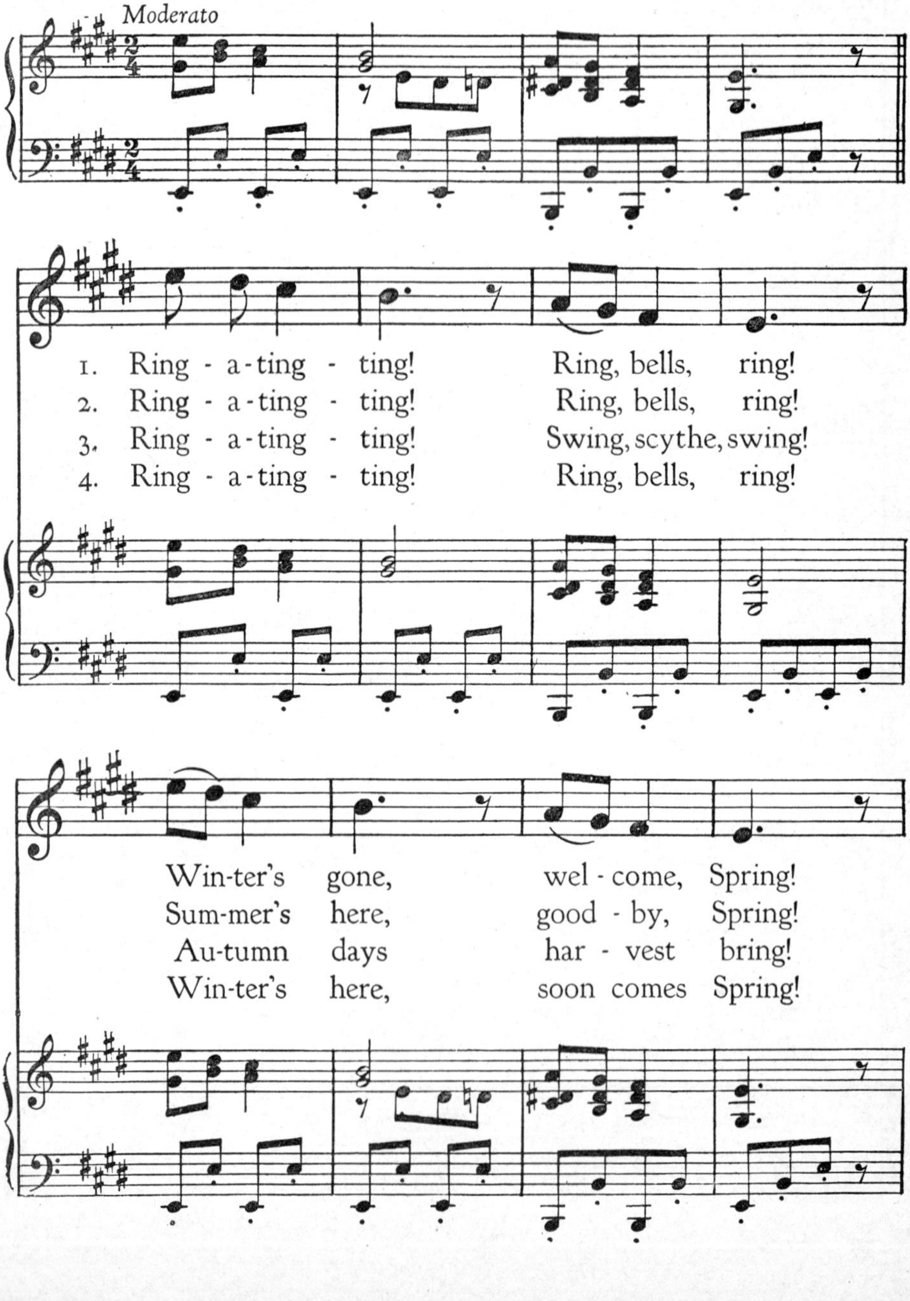
Moderato
1. Ring - a - ting - ting! Ring, bells, ring!
2. Ring - a - ting - ting! Ring, bells, ring!
3. Ring - a - ting - ting! Swing, scythe, swing!
4. Ring - a - ting - ting! Ring, bells, ring!
Win-ter's gone, wel - come, Spring!
Sum-mer's here, good - by, Spring!
Au-tumn days har - vest bring!
Win-ter's here, soon comes Spring!

TICK, TOCK

Sigmund Spaeth
Serbian Folk Song

1. Hark! how the clock is tick-ing! Look how the hands are pick-ing Soft-ly their way thro' the hours of the day!
2. When it is time for sleep-ing, Then how the hands are creep-ing Slow-ly a-round on the face of the clock!

SLUMBER SONG

From the Norwegian

Arranged from Carl Spezier

Lit - tle night wind sigh - ing,
Lit - tle moon - beams stray - ing,

Hush my ba - by cry - ing,
Round his pil - low play - ing,

Fan him with thy dream - y arm,
As you dim your sil - ver beam,

Fairies' Court, by Lee Woodward

WHO'S AT THE DOOR?

25

Not too fast
Breton Melody

Who's that knock-ing at the door,
Who's that ring-ing at the bell,
Rap-a-tap-a-tap, with knuck-les?
Mer-ry as a boot with buck-les?
"I'm the King of Per-i-gord,
"I've a name that none can tell;
Com-ing in the win-ter snow."
Ting-a-ling-a-ling I go."

HAPPY ROSINA

Translated from the French

French Folk Song
Accomp. by J. B. Weckerlin

Good day, hap-py Ro-si-na! In, out, al-ways so gay!

Tell us what you were do-ing, Here, there, bus-y all day!

1. I have been plant-ing my gar - den to - day,
2. I have been feed - ing the spar-rows to - day,
3. I have been play - ing at farm - ing to - day,
4. I have been play - ing at fish - ing to - day,
5. I have been hunt - ing for fair - ies to - day,

Come a-long and play with me, Blos-som-ing May!
Come a-long and sing with me, Song-mak-ing May!
Come a-long and prance with me, Frol-ick-ing May!
Come a-long and play with me, Sun-shin-y May!

Dance

FLAG SONG

Moravian Folk Song

THE SAD STORY OF LITTLE ROBERT

Adapted from the German
Russian Folk Song

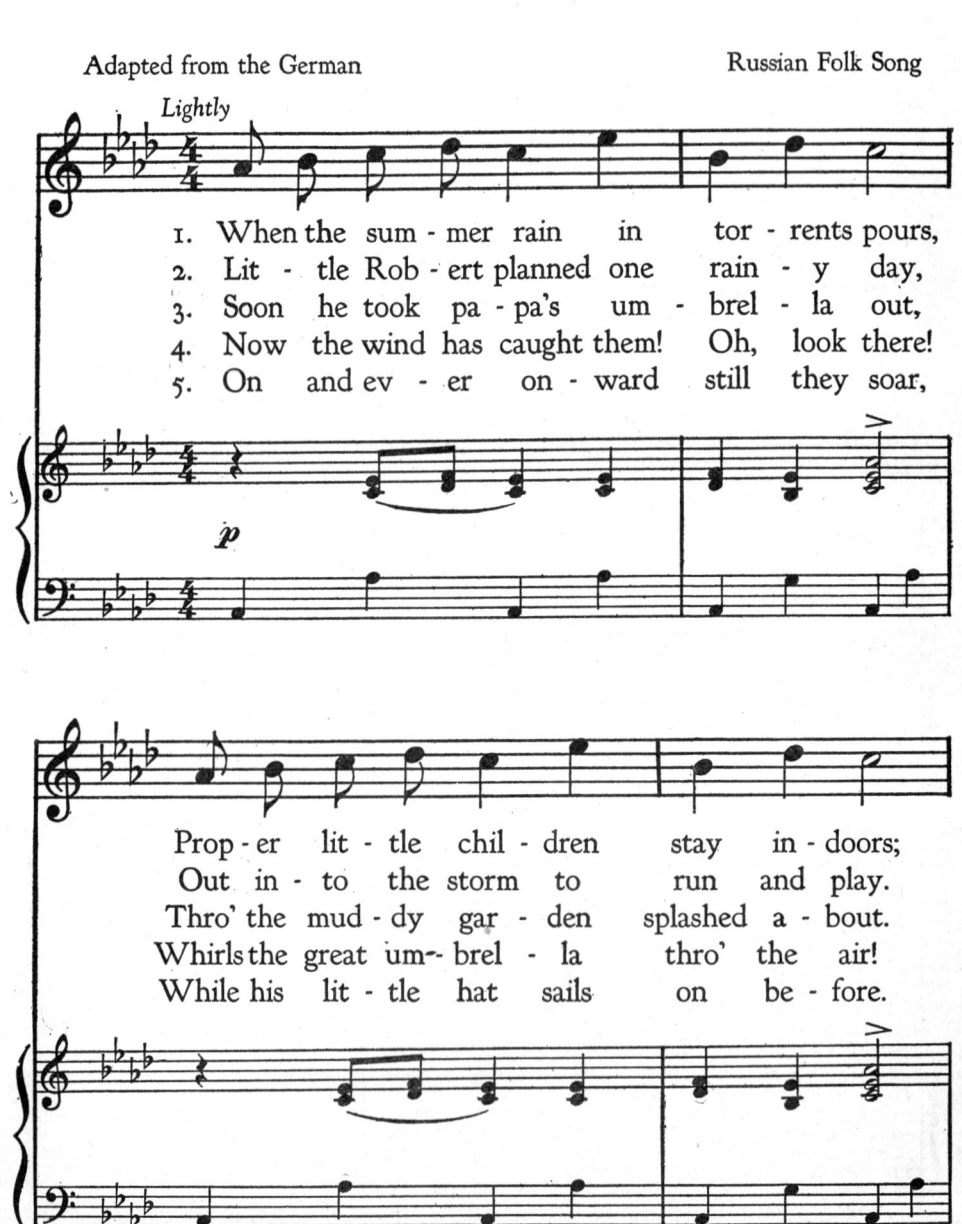

1. When the sum-mer rain in tor-rents pours,
2. Lit-tle Rob-ert planned one rain-y day,
3. Soon he took pa-pa's um-brel-la out,
4. Now the wind has caught them! Oh, look there!
5. On and ev-er on-ward still they soar,

Prop-er lit-tle chil-dren stay in-doors;
Out in-to the storm to run and play.
Thro' the mud-dy gar-den splashed a-bout.
Whirls the great um-brel-la thro' the air!
While his lit-tle hat sails on be-fore.

BUTTERFLY

TEACH US TO PRAY

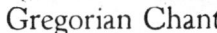
Gregorian Chant

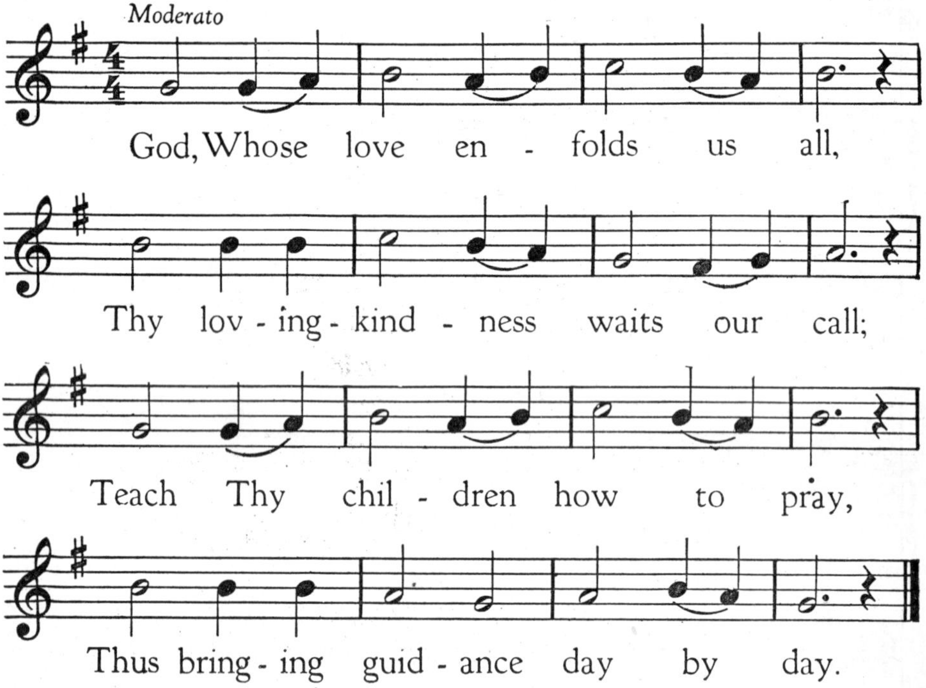

Moderato

God, Whose love en-folds us all,
Thy lov-ing-kind-ness waits our call;
Teach Thy chil-dren how to pray,
Thus bring-ing guid-ance day by day.

A HYMN OF THANKS

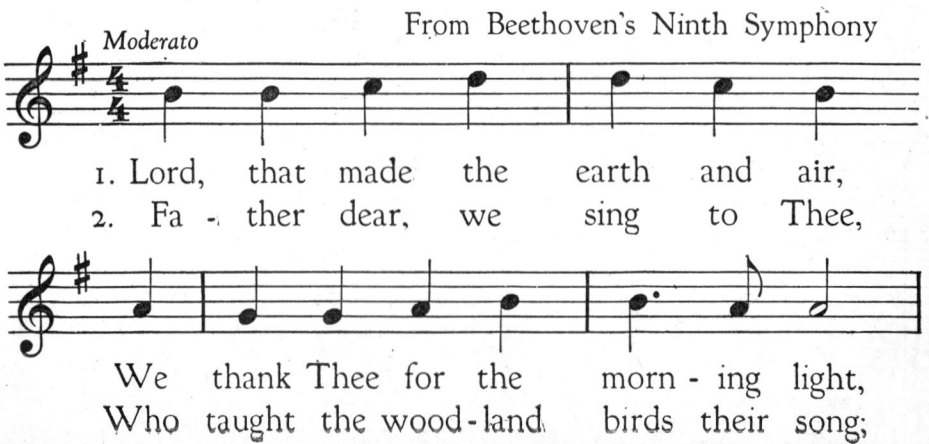
From Beethoven's Ninth Symphony

Moderato

1. Lord, that made the earth and air,
2. Fa-ther dear, we sing to Thee,

We thank Thee for the morn-ing light,
Who taught the wood-land birds their song;

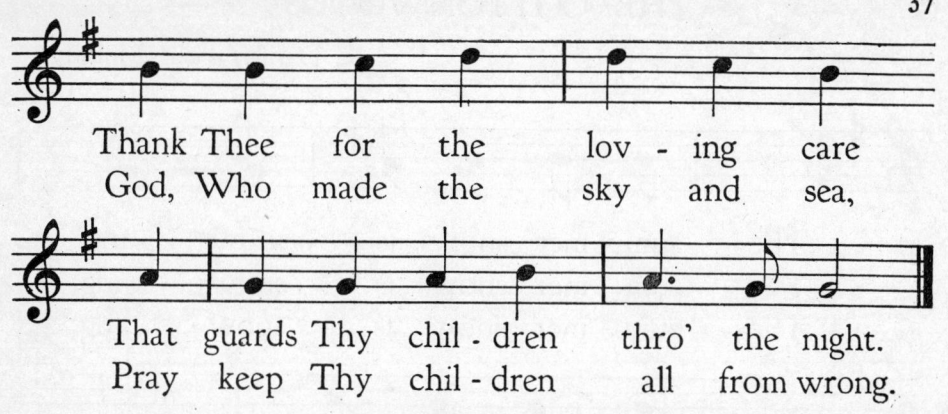

Thank Thee for the lov-ing care
God, Who made the sky and sea,

That guards Thy chil-dren thro' the night.
Pray keep Thy chil-dren all from wrong.

GIFTS OF GOD

Johann Sebastian Bach

Moderato

1. Who has giv'n the sun its bright-ness,
2. Who has taught the birds their mu-sic,

Light-ed stars in eve-ning skies?
Made the for-est breeze re-joice?

All day long, or while we're sleep-ing,
When the breeze and birds are sing-ing,

God is smil-ing thro' their eyes.
What we hear is God's own voice.

THE COTTONWOODS

Danish Folk Melody

Not too fast

1. The sum-mer snow is snow-ing,
2. The sum-mer snow is snow-ing,
3. The sum-mer snow is snow-ing,

It falls up-on the town,
For cot-ton-woods are grand,
But all the world's in bloom;

The chil-dren gay-ly blow-ing
The gi-ant trees be-stow-ing,
The ear-ly ros-es blow-ing

The silk-y milk-white down.
Their treas-ure on the land.
Fill gar-dens with per-fume,

The sum-mer snow is snow-ing.
The sum-mer snow is snow-ing.
Though sum-mer snow is snow-ing.

THE BIRD

Kate Forman

German Folk Song
Used by Brahms

1. There's a sweet bird in the ma-ple tree,
2. Blue is the bird in the ma-ple tree,
3. Milk-white the blooms of the cher-ry tree,

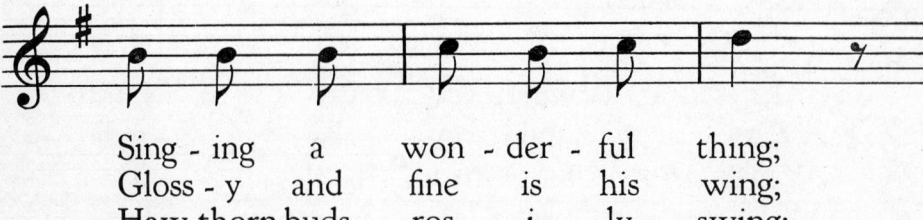

Sing - ing a won - der - ful thing;
Gloss - y and fine is his wing;
Haw-thorn buds ros - i - ly swing;

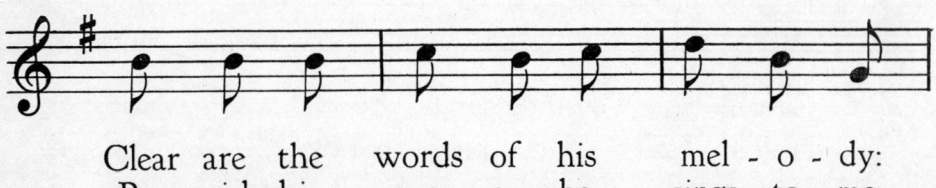

Clear are the words of his mel - o - dy:
Ro - guish his eye as he sings to me:
Buzz - ing and brisk is the hon - ey - bee.

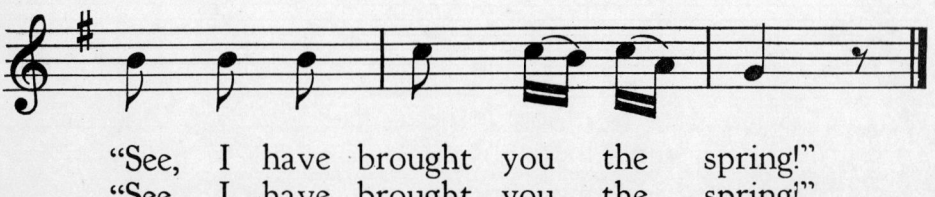

"See, I have brought you the spring!"
"See, I have brought you the spring!"
"See, I have brought you the spring!"

THE WINDMILL

French Folk Song

Smoothly

1. Wind-mill, wind-mill, tall and bus-y,
2. When the winds will play no long-er,
3. Rough-ly puff-ing gales come hith-er,
4. Blow, O winds, a-cross the o-cean,

In the wind-y mead-ow stands,
What a sulk-y, sulk-y, mill!
When they blow from East or West,
Blow up-on the flap-ping hands,

Catch-ing winds that blow a-round it,
Holds its flap-ping hands a-round it,
Wind-mill, wind-mill, tall and bus-y,
Then the mill shall make our sup-per,

With its long and flap-ping hands.
Ver-y stiff and ver-y still.
Al-ways grinds its ver-y best.
In the mead-ow where it stands.

The Mill at Wyk, by Jacob Ruisdael

Seemann & Co., from Rudolf Lesch

THE LITTLE PATH

41

Robert A. Coan
Gayly

A. Maillart
From the opera "The Dragoons of Villars"

1. When the sun's first ray is beam-ing,
2. Where the wood-land brook is sing-ing,
3. Where the gen-tle cows are low-ing,
4. Up the hill and down the hol-low,

When the dew-drops still are gleam-ing,
Where the fra-grant flow'rs are spring-ing,
Where the spic-y breeze is blow-ing,
By the bank where nests the swal-low,

When the drow-sy world is dream-ing,
Where the songs of birds are ring-ing,
By the broad blue riv-er flow-ing,
Lead the way and I will fol-low

Lit-tle path, oh, lead the way!
Lit-tle path, oh, lead the way!
Lit-tle path, oh, lead the way!
All this hap-py hol-i-day!

THE WEATHER VANE

CHRISTMAS

Carl Wilhelm

Quietly

1. Soft and white the snow is blow-ing,
2. "Peace on earth!" those lov-ing voic-es

Like the flut-ter of a wing;
Thro' our hearts for-ev-er ring;

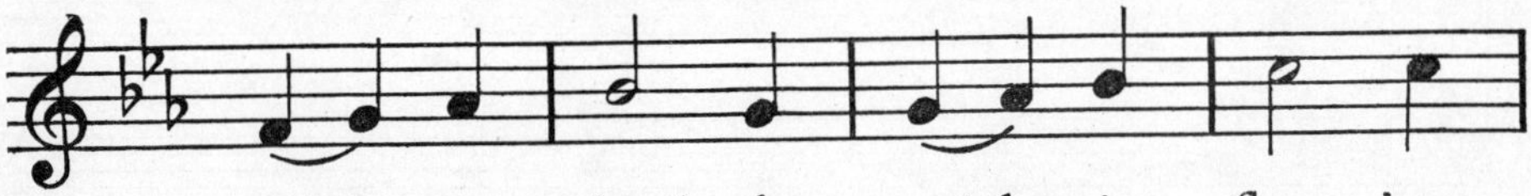

Mu-sic thro' the night is flow-ing,
Heark-en while the night re-joic-es,

Hear the Christ-mas an-gels sing!
Hear the Christ-mas an-gels sing!

A MORNING PRAYER

Folk Tune

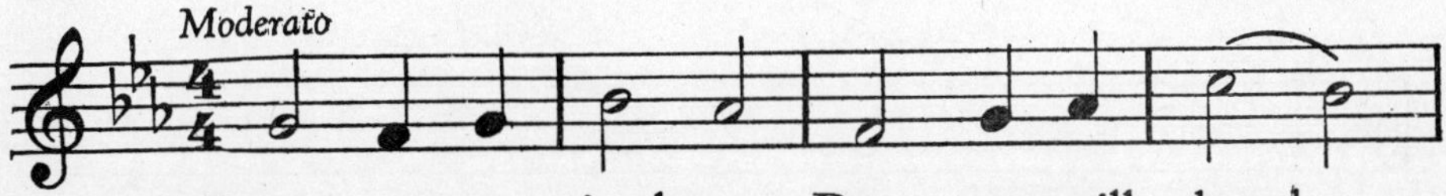

Moderato

1. Dawn at my win-dow, Day soon will break,
2. Dew on the mead-ow, Gold on the hill,

Birds stir in tree tops, And chil-dren all a-wake.
Through all this day, Lord, Help us to do Thy will.

THE SNOW

German Folk Song

Quietly

1. Snow is fall-ing on my gar-den,
2. But the flow'rs are not for-got-ten,

Whirl-ing, danc-ing light-ly down;
Spring will bring them all to light;

Snow is spar-kling on the branch-es
For the frost in dream has traced them

Of the trees tall and brown.
On my win-dow last night.

THE MILL WHEEL

French Melody

Smoothly

1. Dash-ing and splash-ing the mill wheel goes round,
2. "Turn!" cries the mill-er, "Turn fast as you will!

All the world's wait-ing for corn to be ground!
Gold from the mar-ket my pock-ets shall fill."

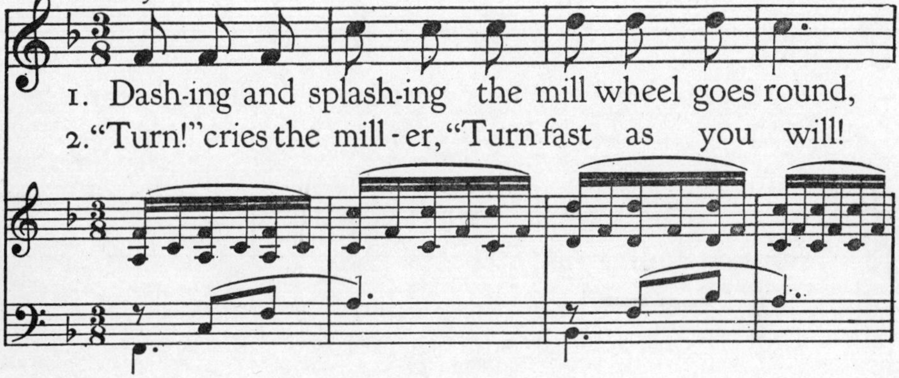

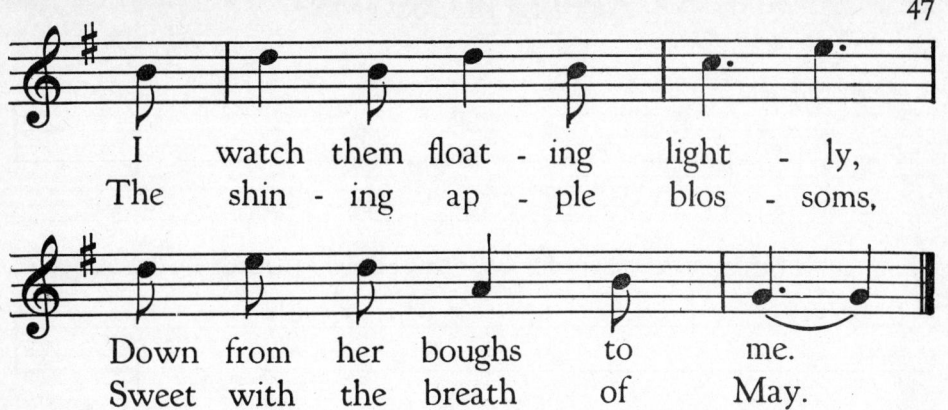

BLUEBIRD, BLUEBIRD

German Folk Song

1. Blue-bird, blue-bird, Joy on your wing!
2. Blue-bird, blue-bird, Makes no re-ply.

No hand would harm you; Why may none charm you
Hap-pi-ly swing-ing, Dream-i-ly sing-ing,

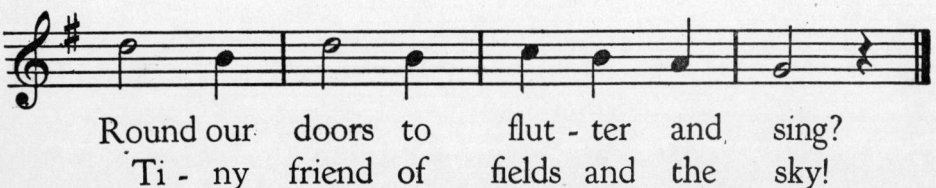

Round our doors to flut-ter and sing?
Ti-ny friend of fields and the sky!

HOT PIES

LITTLE POLLY FLINDERS

THANKSGIVING DAY

51

D. F. E. Auber
From the opera "L'Ambassadrice"

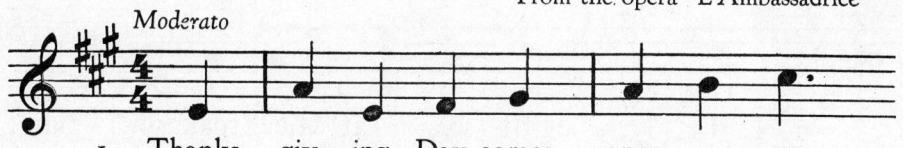

1. Thanks - giv - ing Day comes once a year,
2. When au - tumn har - vests all are done,
3. Then let us think of oth - ers too,

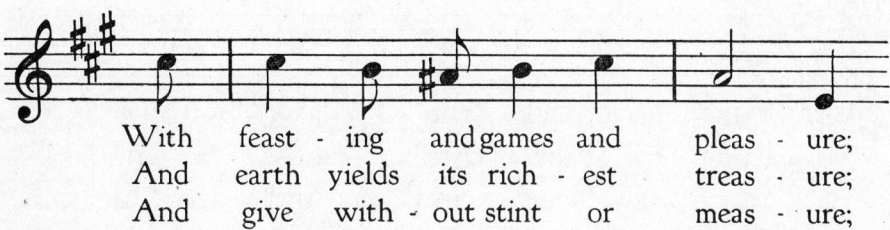

With feast - ing and games and pleas - ure;
And earth yields its rich - est treas - ure;
And give with - out stint or meas - ure;

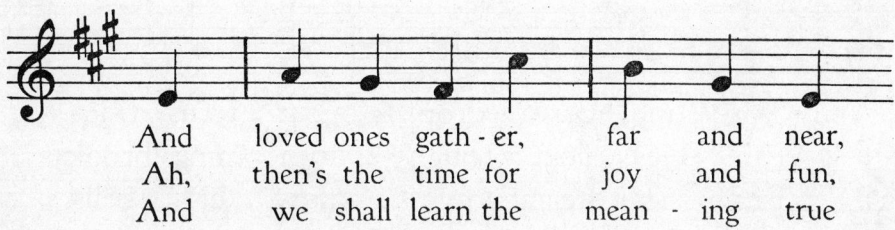

And loved ones gath - er, far and near,
Ah, then's the time for joy and fun,
And we shall learn the mean - ing true

On glad Thanks - giv - ing Day.
On glad Thanks - giv - ing Day.
Of glad Thanks - giv - ing Day

FAIRY SONG

Cecil Cowdrey 　　　　　　　　　　　　　　　　　　Old German

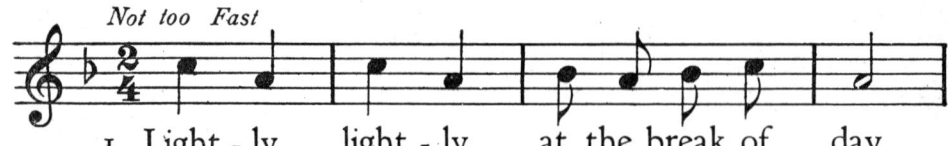

1. Light-ly, light-ly, at the break of day,
2. Stray-ing, stray-ing, with the will-ful breeze,
3. Hid-ing, hid-ing, from the noon-day sun,
4. Skip-ping, skip-ping, to an elf-in tune,

Fair-ies deck the lawn with lace,
Fair-ies flit thro' moss-y nooks,
Fair-ies sleep in hid-den dells,
Fair-ies frol-ic all un-seen.

Shin-ing dew-drop pat-terns trace,
Fair-ies float on run-ning brooks,
Fair-ies dream in flow-er bells,
Who can tell us where they've been,

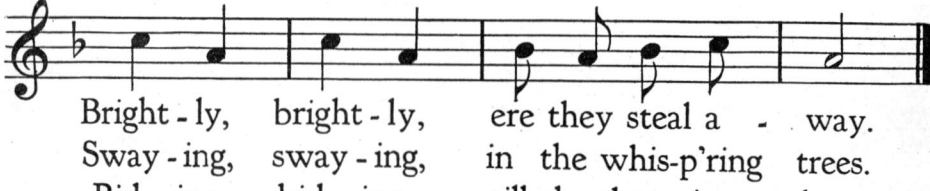

Bright-ly, bright-ly, ere they steal a-way.
Sway-ing, sway-ing, in the whis-p'ring trees.
Bid-ing, bid-ing, till the day is done.
Trip-ping, trip-ping, 'neath the sil-ver moon?

QUESTIONS AND ANSWERS

53

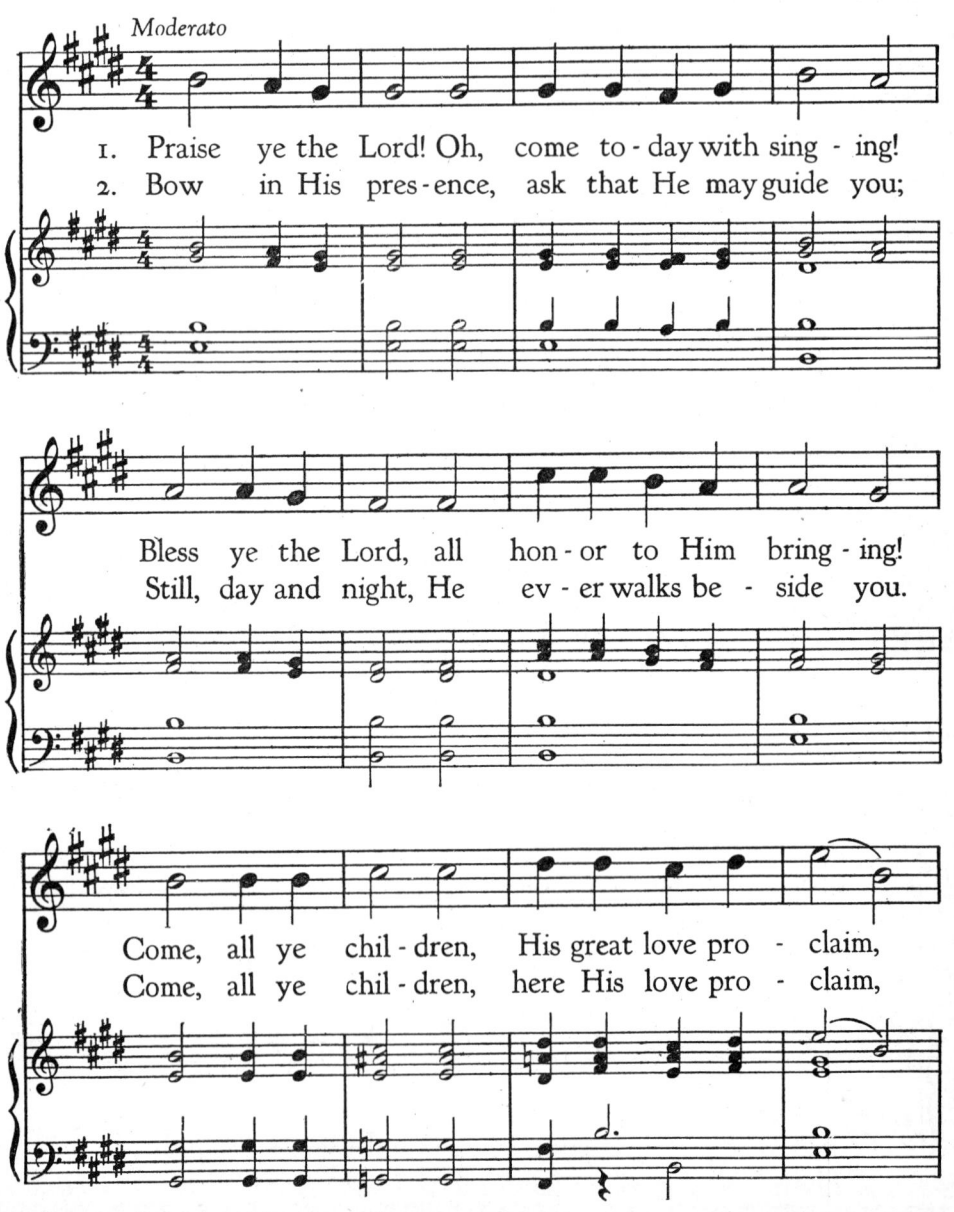

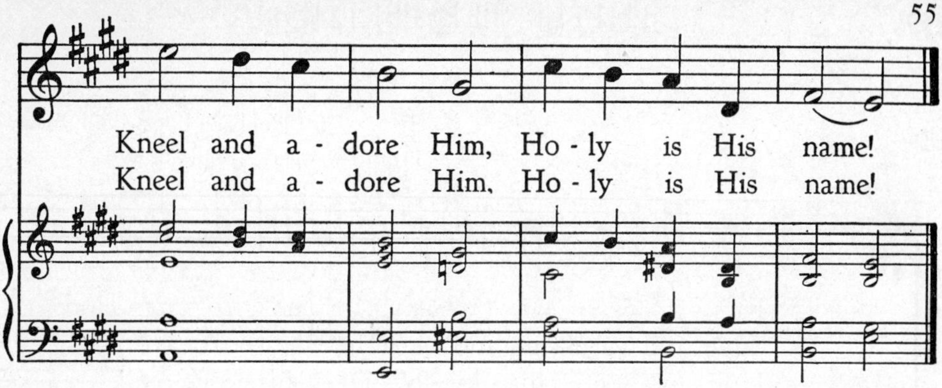

55

Kneel and a-dore Him, Ho-ly is His name!
Kneel and a-dore Him, Ho-ly is His name!

MORNING SONG

Moderato

1. Bless-ed Lord of night and morn-ing,
2. Work-ing, play-ing, may we please Thee,

Keep us safe from harm this day;
Kind in all we do and say!

THE LITTLE ESKIMO

J. Offenbach
From the opera "Boule de Neige"

Not too fast

1. Far a-way, far a-way, In the fro-zen lands,
2. Snug and warm, snug and warm, In a coat of seal,
3. Hus-ky dogs, Hus-ky dogs, Draw his sledge of bones,
4. Home a-gain, home a-gain, He re-turns at last,
5. Far a-way, far a-way, To the fro-zen North,

Where the bit-ing north winds blow,
He is dressed from head to toe;
And they dash o'er ice and snow,
And his face is all a-glow,
In a ship I'd like to go;

CHRISTMAS JOY

C. G. Herring

1. Shin-ing, shin-ing, all the sky is shin-ing,
2. Ring-ing, ring-ing, all the sky is ring-ing,

Stars smil-ing down on earth be-low.
Wel-com-ing in the Christ-mas-tide.

Spar-kling, spar-kling, all the world is spar-kling,
Sing-ing, sing-ing, all the world is sing-ing,

Fir tree and hol-ly, bright with snow.
Birds sing, and bells and folk out-side.

On the earth, and in the sky,
On the earth and in the sky,

Ev-'ry-thing is glad, and so am I.
All things dance for joy and so do I.

HALLOWE'EN

J. Offenbach
From the opera "Boule de Neige"

HUM, HUM, HUM

Kate Forman　　　　　　　　　　　　　　　　German Folk Song

Smoothly

1. Hum, hum, hum! Hear the lit-tle drum!
2. Hum, hum, hum! Lit-tle buzz-er come!
3. Sweet, sweet, sweet! Hon-ey's nice to eat!
4. Hum, hum, hum! Win-ter-time will come!

Ti-ny bees, so young and fun-ny,
Try this clo-ver for a min-ute;
Keep on fly-ing, keep on sip-ping,
So we sup from rose and lil-y,

We won't stop your hunt for hon-ey,
There's a lot of sweet-ness in it.
Fill the combs un-til they're drip-ping.
Till the days are dark and chill-y,

Hum, hum, hum! Hear the lit-tle drum!
Hum, hum, hum! Lit-tle buzz-er come!
Sweet, sweet, sweet! Hon-ey's nice to eat!
Hum, hum, hum! Win-ter-time will come!

HONEYBEE

Adapted from the German
German Folk Song
Brightly

1. Hon-ey-bee, hon-ey-bee, far from home,
2. But-ter-fly, but-ter-fly, fold your wing!
3. Ka-ty-did, ka-ty-did, all is still,

Round a-bout, in and out, how you roam!
How it glows, on the rose as you swing!
On the lea, in the tree, on the hill.

Fly a-way, fly a-way, don't you hear?
Fly a-way, fly a-way, don't you hear?
Sing your rime, it is time, nev-er fear,

Hon-ey-bee, hon-ey-bee, night is near.
But-ter-fly, but-ter-fly, night is near.
Ka-ty-did, ka-ty-did, night is here.

THE HARVEST HOME

English Game Song

1. Sow, sow, the shin - ing grain!
2. Guard, guard, the spring - ing grain,
3. Reap, reap, the rip - ened grain,

Heav'n will send it sun and rain.
Ris - ing green from earth a - gain!
Let no gold - en sheaf re - main!

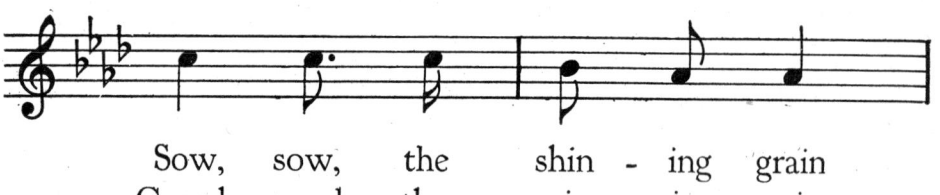

Sow, sow, the shin - ing grain
Guard, guard, the spring - ing grain
Reap, reap, the rip - ened grain

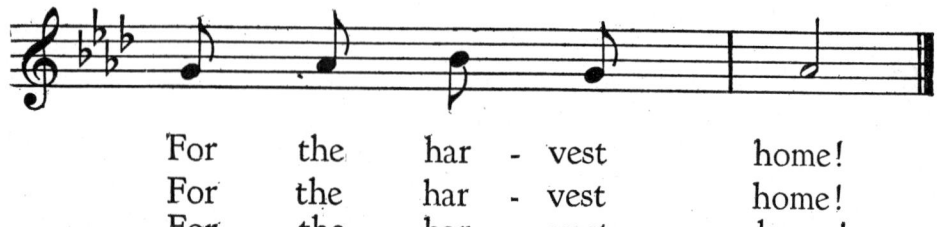

For the har - vest home!
For the har - vest home!
For the har - vest home!

COME OUT, ELVES AND FAIRIES

Engelbert Humperdinck

Gracefully

1. Come out, elves and fair-ies, And dance on the green! A-wake at the will Of Ti-tan-ia, our queen. We'll
   cow-slips are dream-ing, On lawns bright with dew, The toad and the crick-et Make mu-sic for you. We'll
   glow-worm has dark-ened His lamp on the hill, The pip-ers are si-lent, The danc-ers are still. Ere

WHAT SHALL I SING?

Mother Goose *(first stanza)*   Adapted from an English Folk Song

Lively

1. Sing! Sing! What shall I sing?
2. Play! Play! Where shall I play?
3. Laugh! Laugh! What if he does?

The cat has eat-en the pud-ding string.
It's rain-ing out in the fields to-day.
The birds are hap-py and bees go "Buzz!"

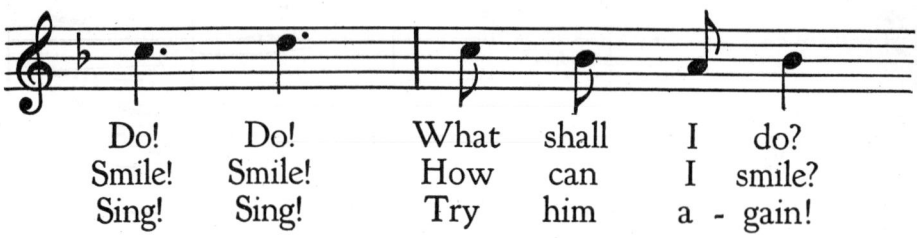

Do! Do! What shall I do?
Smile! Smile! How can I smile?
Sing! Sing! Try him a-gain!

The cat has bit-ten it quite in two!
My broth-er teas-es me all the while.
Per-haps you'll find him a good boy then.

HEEL AND TOE

67

Kate Forman

Used by Humperdinck in "Hansel and Gretel"

Lively

1. Here we come, and here we go;
2. Mu - sic sounds with meas - ured beat,
3. Ti - ny ones, that hard - ly know

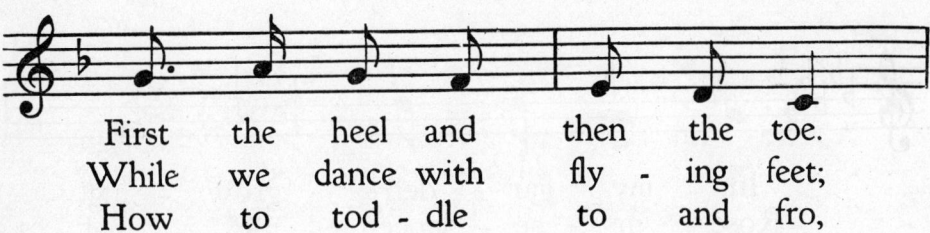

First the heel and then the toe.
While we dance with fly - ing feet;
How to tod - dle to and fro,

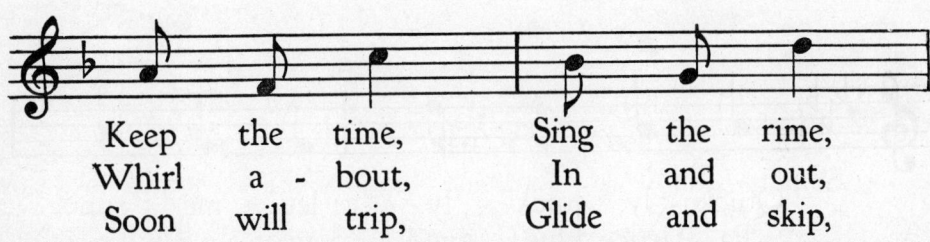

Keep the time, Sing the rime,
Whirl a - bout, In and out,
Soon will trip, Glide and skip,

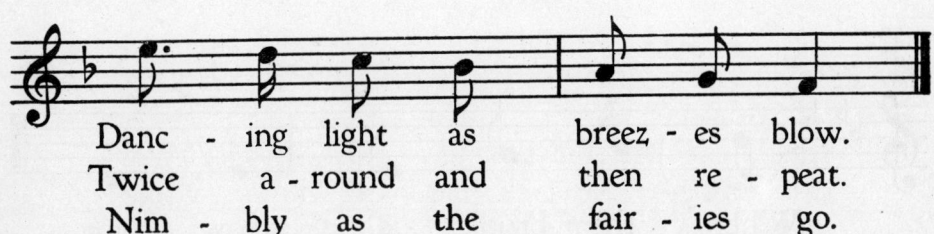

Danc - ing light as breez - es blow.
Twice a - round and then re - peat.
Nim - bly as the fair - ies go.

THE THIRSTY FLOWERS

Translated from the German   K. A. Kern

1. You are thirst-y, pret-ty flow'rs,
2. I will fetch you wa-ter cool,
3. See, the draft al-read-y here!

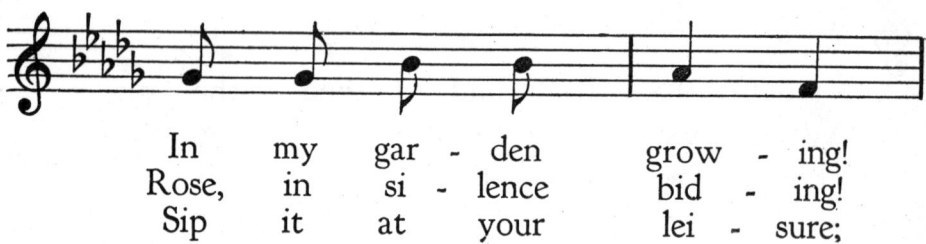

In my gar-den grow-ing!
Rose, in si-lence bid-ing!
Sip it at your lei-sure;

Quick-ly, quick-ly, let me run
Pa-tience, blue-eyed vi-o-lets,
Blos-som all the sum-mer long,

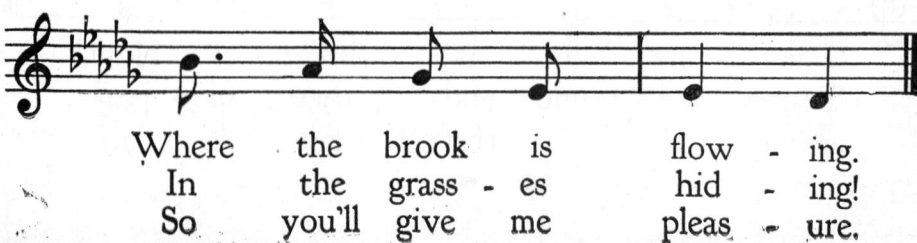

Where the brook is flow-ing.
In the grass-es hid-ing!
So you'll give me pleas-ure.

THE MOTHER, by Pieter de Hooch

CRADLE SONG

69

Oh, the fun of skat - ing,
Light - ly as a feath - er,
Sing it in a song!
Skat - ing as we go!

THE SNOWBIRD

Carl Wilhelm

1. Snow - bird, snow - bird, friend of good cheer,
2. Snow - bird, snow - bird, haste to my door,
3. Snow - bird, snow - bird, perched on the tree,

Wild winds are call - ing, White flakes are fall - ing,
Fear - less - ly trip - ping, Joy - ful - ly skip - ping!
Cheer - i - ly cling - ing, Mer - ri - ly swing - ing,

Snow - bird, snow - bird, win - ter is here!
Here are crumbs in boun - ti - ful store.
Sing your song of glad - ness for me!

A SONG OF FAIRIES

Adapted from
Wm. M. Thackeray

Polish Folk Song

1. Once in the twi-light, on my moth-er's knee,
Sweet tales of Faer-ie she would tell to me;
Then at night as I lay sleep-ing,
Fair-ies came on bright wing sweep-ing,
Came to vis-it me.

2. Dream-ing I watched them fly from east to west;
Bright gifts they brought me where I lay at rest.
Gone are all those fair-ies gleam-ing;
Would that I a-gain were dream-ing,
On my moth-er's breast!

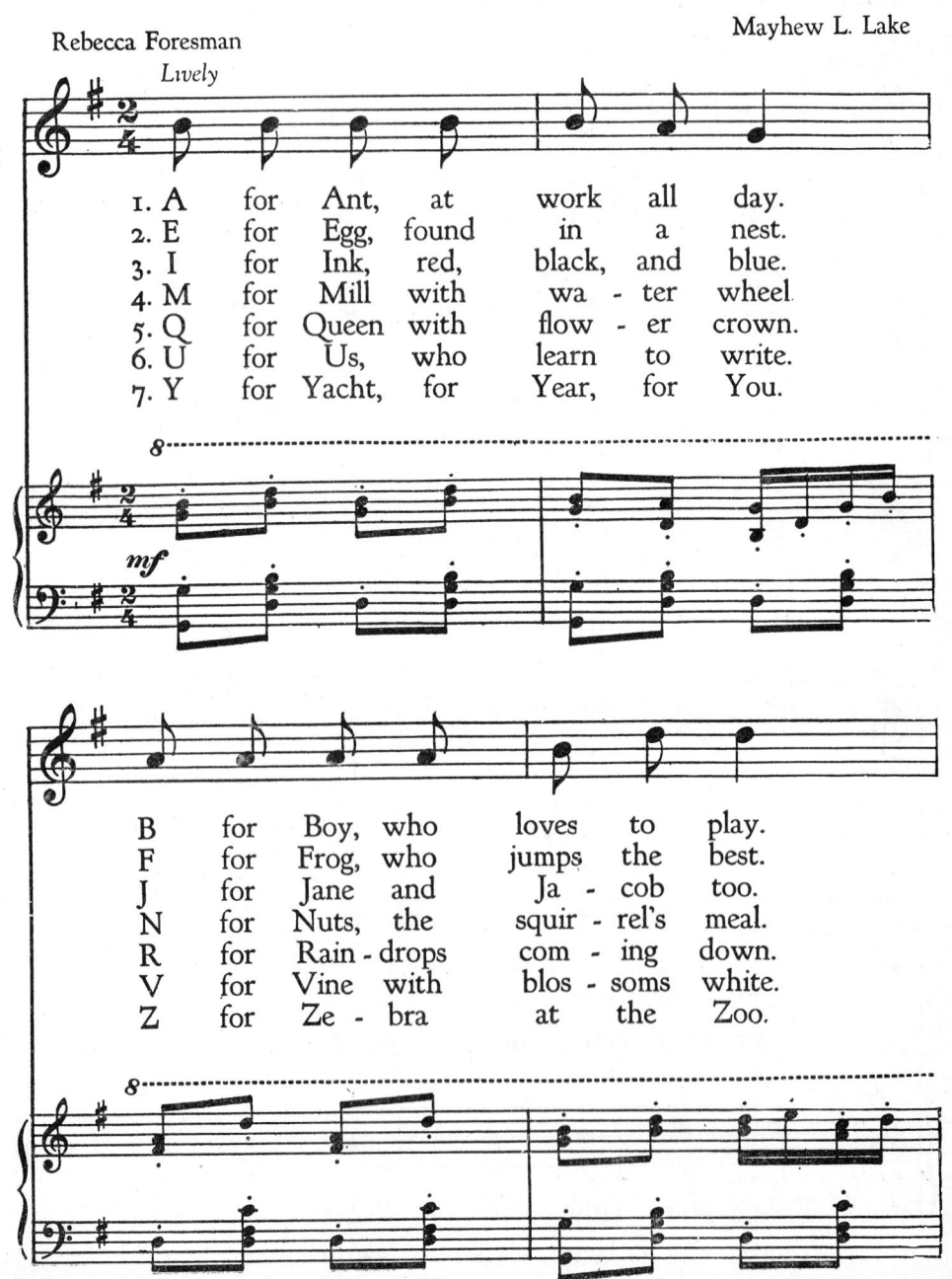

SHIPS

HOT CROSS-BUNS

Old English
Old Song

1. Hot cross-buns! The bak-er man is here to-day.
2. Hot cross-buns! Per-haps you'll find a rai-sin too.
3. Hot cross-buns! The bak-er has a love-ly store.

Hot cross-buns! A cent a-piece is all we pay.
Hot cross-buns! If not, a cur-rant has to do.
Hot cross-buns! He makes the buns the night be-fore.

Some are made with cit-ron sliced.
Melt-ed sug-ar on the crust,
Bak-er's buns are nev-er hot,

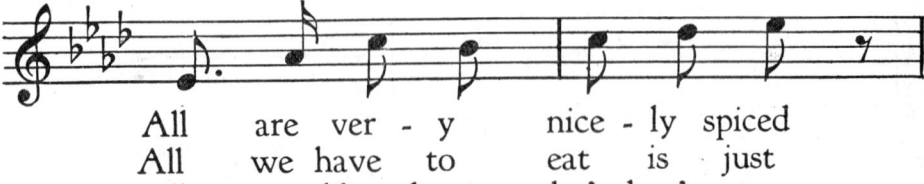

All are ver-y nice-ly spiced
All we have to eat is just
Still we like them, tho' they're not

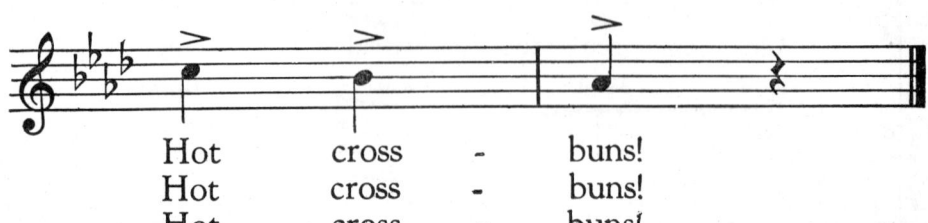

Hot cross - buns!
Hot cross - buns!
Hot cross - buns!

THE ECHO

French Game Tune

1. Out in the woods I know a lit-tle sprite,
2. He loves to talk and chat-ter all the day,
3. And when I scold, it seems to make him mad;

But he is al-ways hid-den out of sight.
But just re-peats what-ev-er I may say,
But if I speak more gen-tly, he is glad.

Would you be-lieve I've nev-er seen his face,
And if I sing, he does it just the same,
One day I cried, "Please come and shov-el snow!"

Al-tho' he seems to live a-round the place?
So I sup-pose he takes it for a game.
He un-der-stood, be-cause he shout-ed, "No!"

THE PARADE

R. A. C.
F. A. Boïeldieu
From the opera "La Dame Blanche"

1. Hark, hark to the roll-ing drum!
2. Hark, hark to the pierc-ing fife!
3. Hark, hark to the bu-gle's call!
4. Faint-er, ev-er faint-er still,

Faint-ly and far it is sound-ing now.
Loud-ly and shrill it is sound-ing now.
Gay-ly and clear it is sound-ing now.
Soft-ly and dis-tant are sound-ing now,

See, see, here the sol-diers come,
Hap-py is the sol-dier's life,
See, there goes the bu-gler tall,
Bu-gle, drum, and fife so shrill,

Ban-ners wav-ing high.
March-ing proud-ly by.
Blow-ing the re-treat.
Pass-ing down the street.

THE SOLDIER BOY

Old English Tune

1. Sol - dier, sol - dier, brave and strong,
2. Sol - dier, sol - dier, straight and tall,
3. Sol - dier, sol - dier, true and fine,

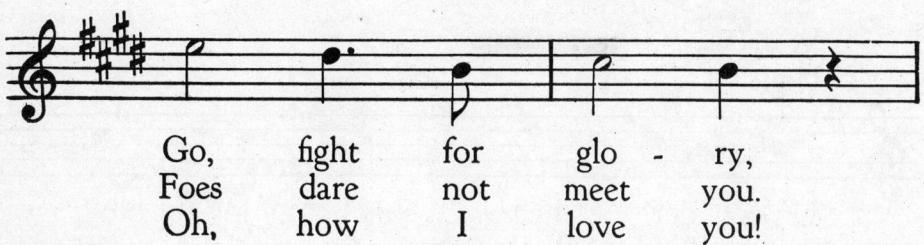

Go, fight for glo - ry,
Foes dare not meet you.
Oh, how I love you!

March - ing, march - ing, all day long,
Here, at home, you'll find us all,
Ev - er faith - ful friend of mine,

Then bring me back a sto - ry.
With wav - ing flags to greet you.
May Heav - en watch a - bove you!

A SOLDIER TRUE

Folk Song

EASTER CAROL

Old German

1. Ring, far bells, ring, clear bells, this glad East-er dawn!
2. Bright blos-soms are bud-ding for joy in the field.

Oh, ring in the sun-rise, earth's shad-ows are gone!
The grain, fresh-ly spring-ing, a - bun-dance shall yield.

The whole world is gay. Be-gone, then, dis - may!
Ring out, bells, on high! Ring far thro' the sky!

Ring, far bells, ring, clear bells, this glad East-er day!
Ye peo-ple re - joic - ing, in wor-ship draw nigh!

THE YOUNG MUSICIAN

Kate Forman

Old Swabian Folk Song

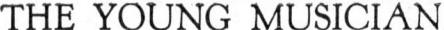

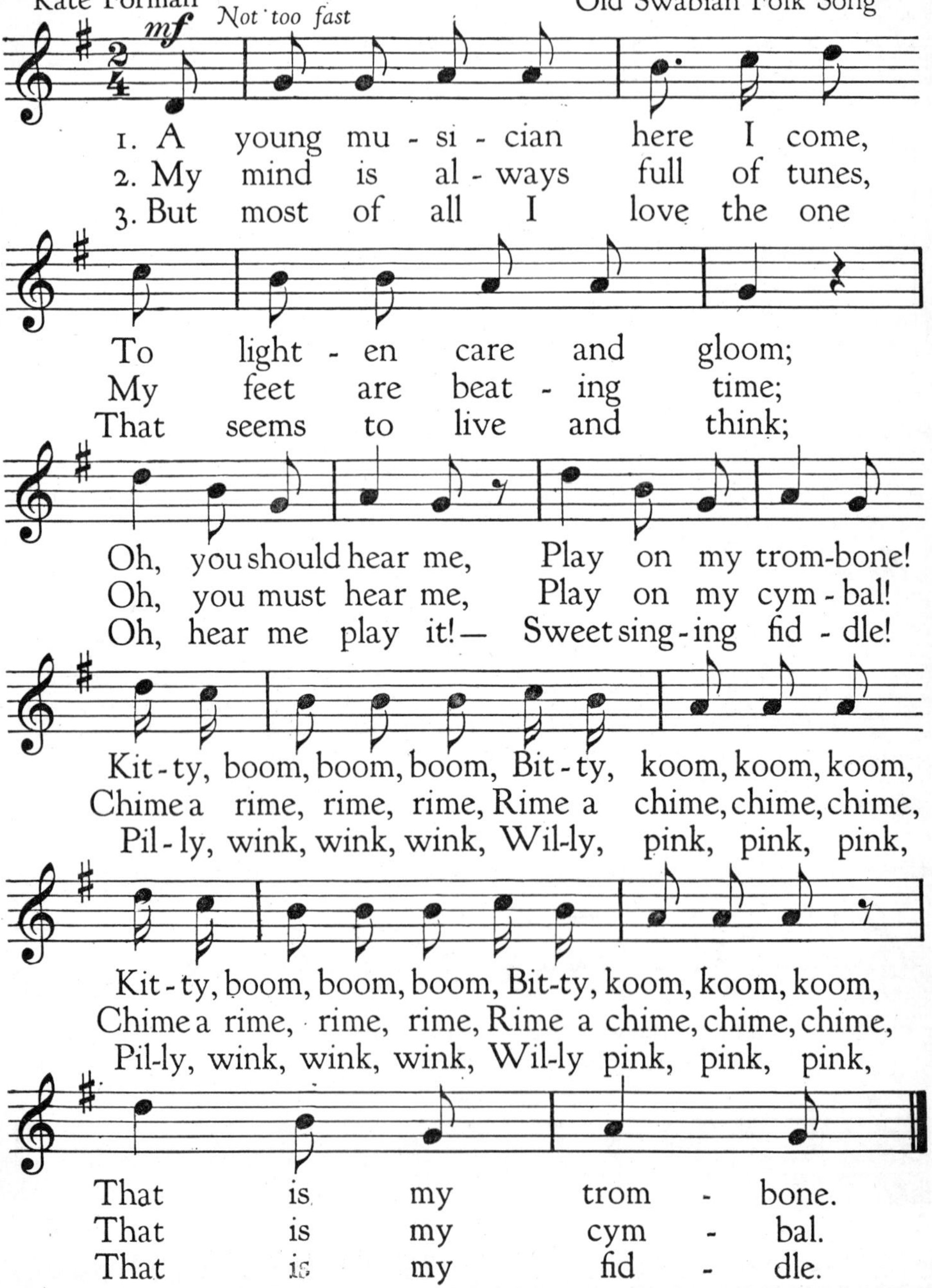

THE SINGING BOYS, by Franz Hals

SLEEP, BABY, SLEEP

87

Folk Song

1. Sleep, ba - by, sleep!
2. Sleep, ba - by, sleep!

Thy fa - ther minds his sheep;
The sky is full of sheep;

Thy moth - er shakes the dream - land tree,
The stars are lamb - kins soft and white,

And lit - tle dreams fall down on thee.
A shep - herd - ess the moon so bright.

Sleep, ba - by, sleep!
Sleep, ba - by, sleep!

BAKING A CAKE

Grace Hall
Russian Folk Song

Not too fast

1. Moth-er dear, make a cake! Please let us help you bake!
2. Sug-ar and but-ter mix; Milk and eggs, five or six?
3. When it is brown and crisp, Take from the broom a wisp,
4. Oh, such a glo-rious cake! Moth-er dear, may we take
5. Now all the loaf is gone, Not a crumb left, not one!

Let us bring all that will help make it nice.
Stir in the flour, as much as you may choose.
Stab the high loaf! It comes out dry and neat!
Each a big slice of this won-der-ful sweet?
Nev-er, in all the world, was such a cake!

Here's flour, sug-ar, but-ter, spice, Fresh eggs, a doz-en!
Now in-to the pan it goes; Then in the ov-en.
Now put it up-on a plate; Then on the ta-ble.
For once, we should like to eat All we are a-ble.
And now, Moth-er, let us make Just such an-oth-er!

MAY DAY

Translated from the French
French Folk Song
Gayly

1. This is the first of May, Tra la la,   Tra la la,
2. All round the May-pole tall, Tra la la,   Tra la la,
3. Next choose the fair-est maid, Tra la la,   Tra la la,
4. All boys and girls join in, Tra la la,   Tra la la,

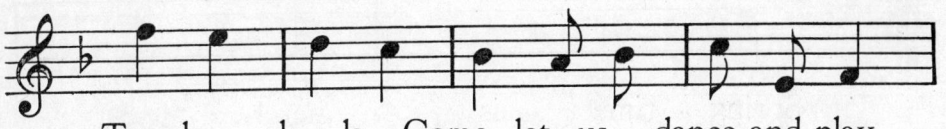

Come, sing a roun-de-lay, Come, let us dance and play,
Gath-er we one and all, For our gay fes-ti-val,
One who is not a-fraid, Our choice must be o-beyed,
Take hands around the green, Dance round our lovely Queen,

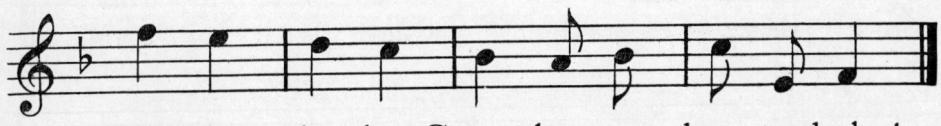

Tra la   la la, Come, let us   dance and play,
Tra la   la la, For our gay   fes-ti-val,
Tra la   la la, Our choice must be   o-beyed,
Tra la   la la, Dance round our love-ly Queen,

Tra la   la la, Come, let us   dance and play!
Tra la   la la, For our gay   fes-ti-val.
Tra la   la la, Our choice must be   o-beyed.
Tra la   la la, Dance round our love-ly Queen.

All the world is Won - der - land,
All the world is Won - der - land,

Spring - time is here!
Spring - time is here!

MORNING HYMN OF PRAISE

Folk Tune

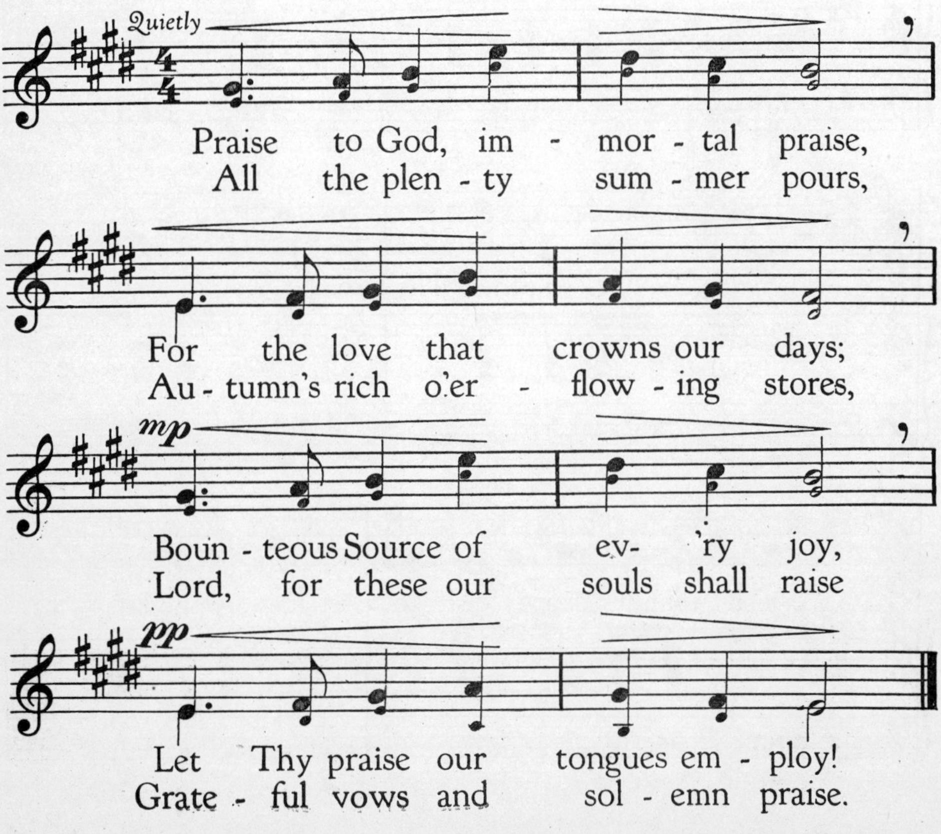

Quietly

Praise to God, im - mor - tal praise,
All the plen - ty sum - mer pours,

For the love that crowns our days;
Au - tumn's rich o'er - flow - ing stores,

Boun - teous Source of ev - 'ry joy,
Lord, for these our souls shall raise

Let Thy praise our tongues em - ploy!
Grate - ful vows and sol - emn praise.

THE TINY LITTLE WOOD

Grace Hall. French Folk Song

1. Far, oh, far a-way, O-ver hill and o-ver dale,
2. Hid with-in the wood, O'er the hill and o'er the dale,
3. There up-on the tree, In the wood be-yond the hill,

Far, oh, far a-way, O-ver hill and o-ver dale,
Hid with-in the wood, O'er the hill and o'er the dale,
There up-on the tree, In the wood be-yond the hill,

Grows a lit-tle wood, Grows a wood all cool and shad-y,
Hid with-in the wood Stands a ti-ny sil-ver beech tree,
Grows a lit-tle branch, Grows a ti-ny twig and slen-der,

Grows a ti-ny wood, That for a-ges there has stood.
Stands a sil-ver beech, Just as high as you can reach.
Grows a ti-ny twig, That is on-ly just so big

4. There up-on the branch Of the tree with-in the wood,
5. Oh, the lit-tle nest On the branch up-on the tree,
6. Now, the lit-tle note In the nest up-on the branch,

There up-on the branch Of the tree with-in the wood,
Oh, the lit-tle nest On the branch up-on the tree,
Now, the lit-tle note In the nest up-on the branch,

Lies a lit-tle nest, Lies a ti-ny nest so down-y,
Holds a lit-tle note, Holds a ti-ny note that's fold-ed,
Hides a ti-ny word—You will find it if you seek it.

Lies a down-y nest, Where a ti-ny bird may rest.
Fold-ed straight and neat, And ad-dressed to you, my sweet!
Read it to the end: "I'm your true and lov-ing friend!"

With their shoulders back and hands just so,
Ev-ry foot marks time to beat of drum,
In a jol-ly tune we love to hear,
While the drum-mers drum and fif-ers blow,

While the Cap-tain is com-mand-ing.
For the march-ing or-der read-y.
As they march a-long be-fore us.
As a-long we're gay-ly swing-ing!

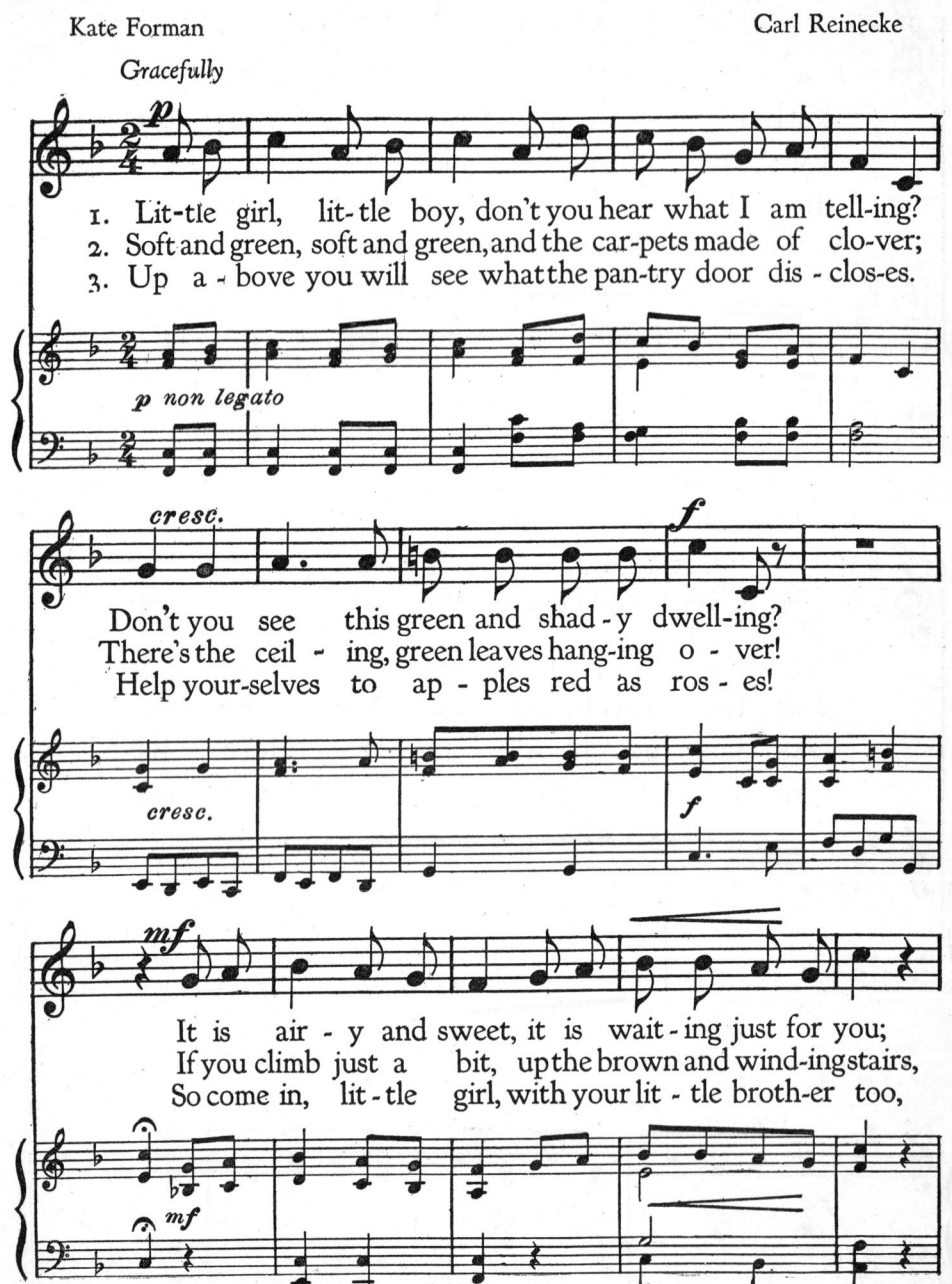

dim.
Make it your home, Oh, my lit - tle chil - dren, do!
There you may rest in the co - zi - est of chairs.
Rob - ins are sing - ing a sweet good day to you.

MARKET DAY

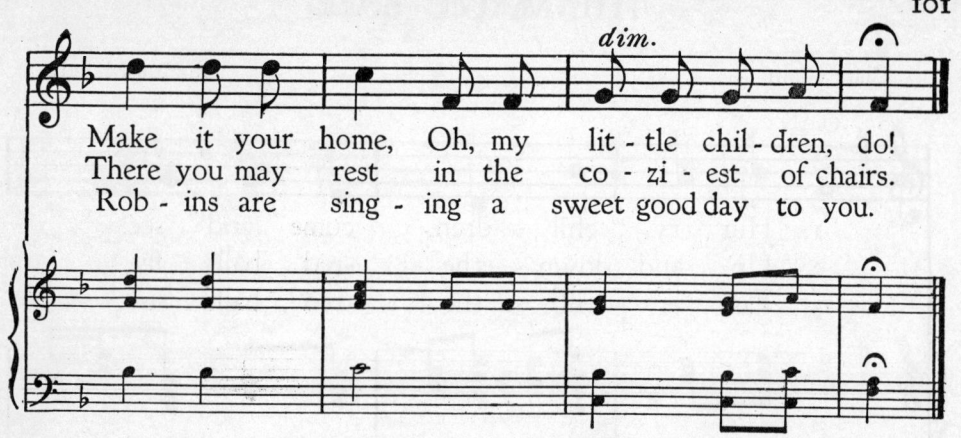

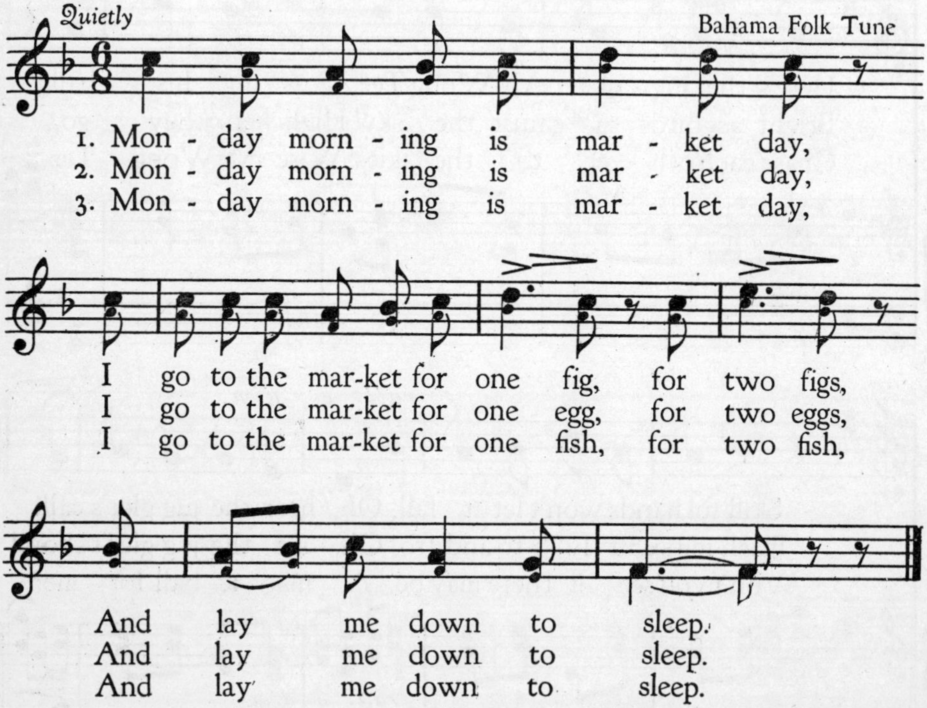
Quietly
Bahama Folk Tune
1. Mon - day morn - ing is mar - ket day,
2. Mon - day morn - ing is mar - ket day,
3. Mon - day morn - ing is mar - ket day,
I go to the mar-ket for one fig, for two figs,
I go to the mar-ket for one egg, for two eggs,
I go to the mar-ket for one fish, for two fish,
And lay me down to sleep.
And lay me down to sleep.
And lay me down to sleep.

PLANT A TREE

With dignity   W. A. Mozart

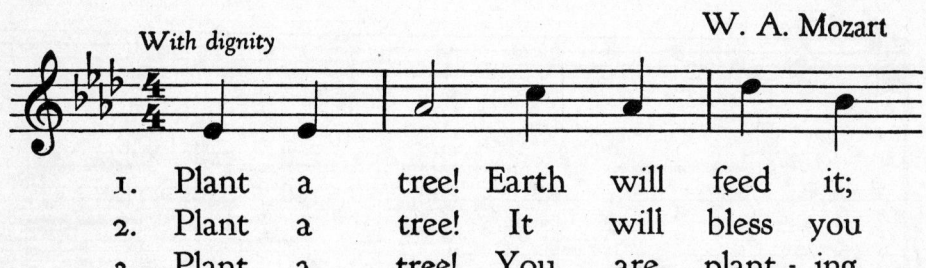

1. Plant a tree! Earth will feed it;
2. Plant a tree! It will bless you
3. Plant a tree! You are plant-ing

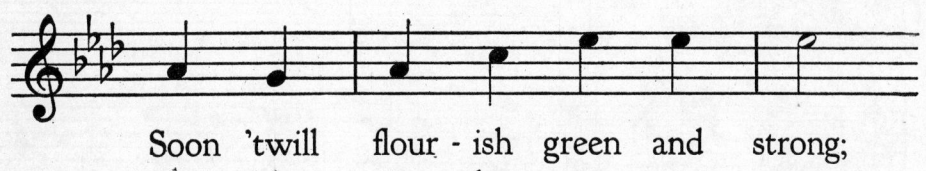

Soon 'twill flour-ish green and strong;
In the years that are to come;
What a thou-sand men may see;

Soon 'twill spread its peace-ful shad-ow,
Plant it glad-ly, it will serve you;
House and raf-ter, ship and mast-head,

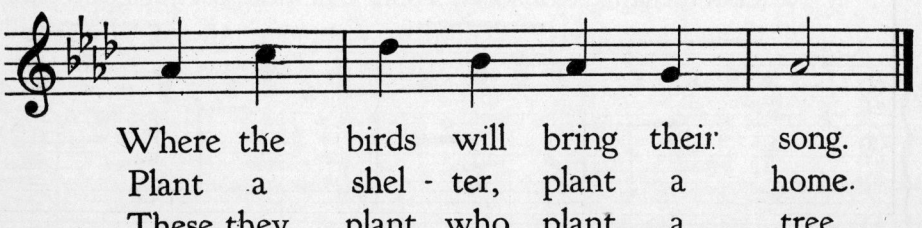

Where the birds will bring their song.
Plant a shel-ter, plant a home.
These they plant who plant a tree.

Round my pil-low her watch to keep.
From the east you come sail-ing back.

When the sun glanc-es in at dawn,
La-dy Moon, let me jour-ney too,

rall. - - - molto

La-dy Moon is al-ways gone!
Round the world and back with you.

THE POSTILION

William Taubert

1. I'll be a gay pos - til - ion, Four pranc-ing po-nies guide;
They'll hear my mer-ry bu - gle In many a coun-try-side.

2. In sleep-y town and vil - lage, A live - ly tune I'll blow;
With long whip gay-ly snap-ping, Thro' all the land we'll go.

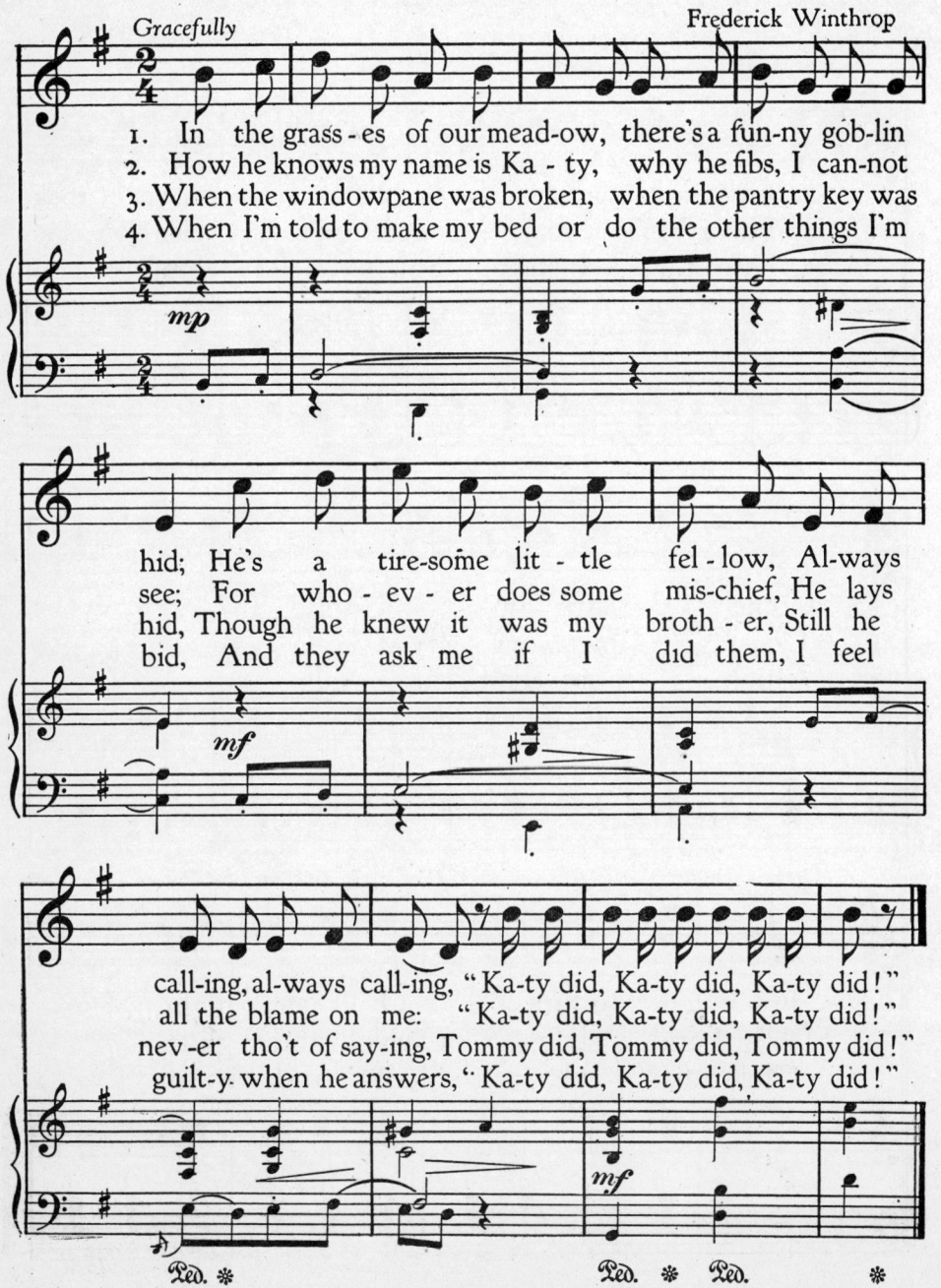

SKATING

P. Lacome

MY VALENTINE

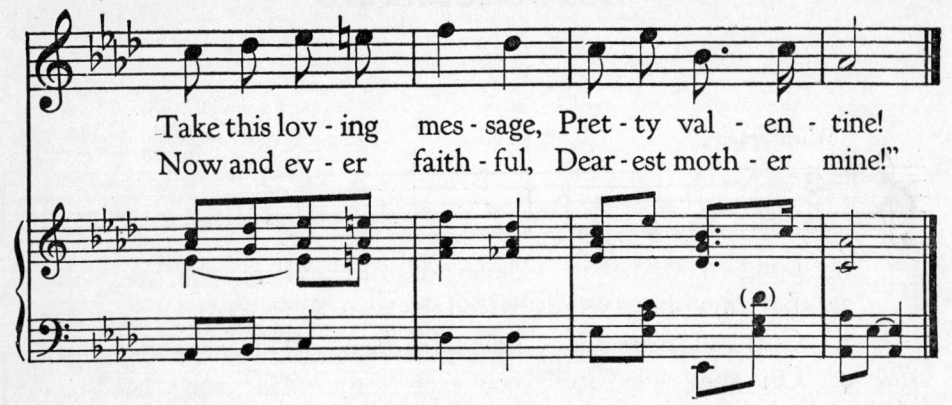

SPRING SONG

Giuseppe Verdi
From the opera "Don Carlos"

Gayly

1. Come and sing! Let your voic - es so glad - ly ring!
2. Play and song To the spring, jo-vial spring, be - long.

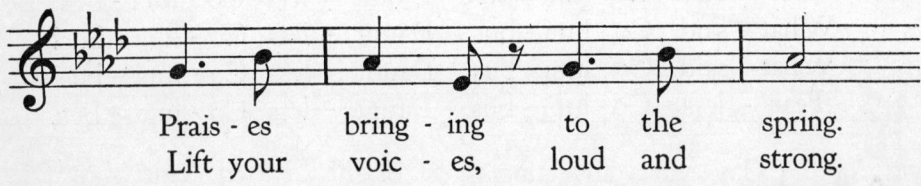

Prais - es bring - ing to the spring.
Lift your voic - es, loud and strong.

Joy - ous, hap - py spring-time, Birds are on the wing.
Hearts are gay in spring-time, Join our hap - py throng!

COLUMBUS

C. W. Gluck

1. Long a-go in days of old, O'er the sea a
2. Baf-fling head winds barred the way, Storms roared o'er the
3. Cra-ven fears as-sailed his men, Till they turned to
4. On they sailed and ev-er on, Till at last their

sail - or bold Steered where un-known wa - ters rolled;
wa - ters gray, Calms de-layed them day by day;
cow - ards, then, Begged to seek their homes a - gain;
voyage was done, Till at last their goal was won;

Fear - less Co - lum - bus, Daunt - less Co - lum - bus
What said Co - lum - bus, Daunt - less Co - lum - bus?
What said Co - lum - bus, Daunt - less Co - lum - bus?
Fear - less Co - lum - bus, Daunt - less Co - lum - bus,

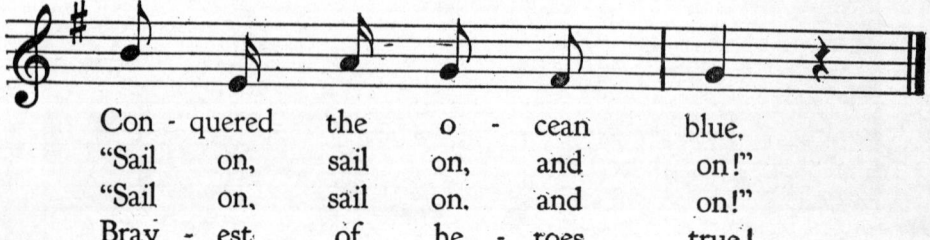

Con - quered the o - cean blue.
"Sail on, sail on, and on!"
"Sail on, sail on, and on!"
Brav - est of he - roes true!

The Boy Columbus, by John Whiting

CHRISTMAS HYMN

GOD OF MERCY

H. Neele
German Chorale

1. God of mercy throned on high,
2. Young and erring trav-'lers we,
3. Let us ever hear Thy voice,

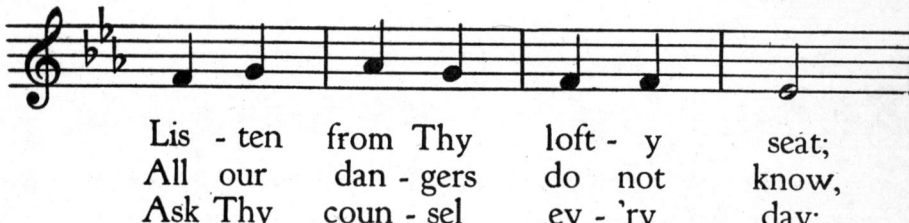

Listen from Thy lofty seat;
All our dangers do not know,
Ask Thy counsel ev-'ry day;

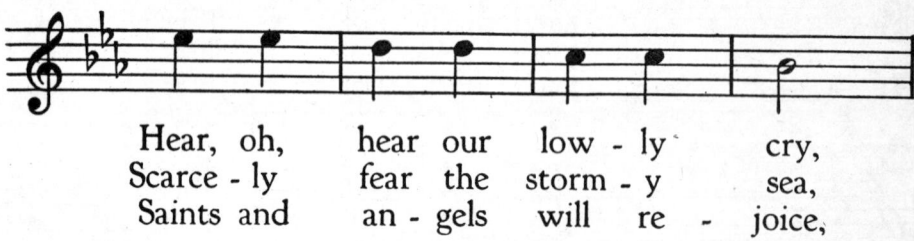

Hear, oh, hear our lowly cry,
Scarcely fear the stormy sea,
Saints and angels will rejoice,

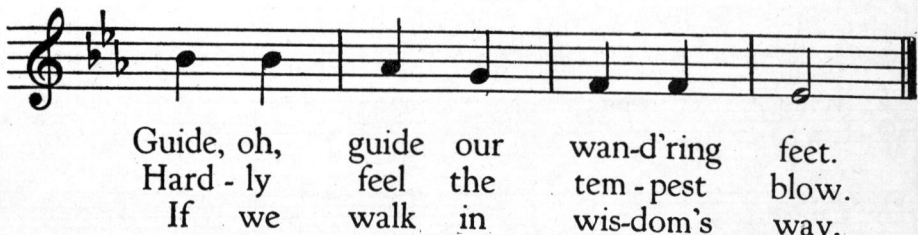

Guide, oh, guide our wand'ring feet.
Hardly feel the tempest blow.
If we walk in wisdom's way.

THE STAR-SPANGLED BANNER

121

Francis Scott Key

John Stafford Smith

TOPICAL INDEX

Songs for Columbus Day
	PAGE
Flag Song	30-31
Ships	77
A Soldier True	83
Columbus	116

Songs for Hallowe'en
Who's at the Door	25
Hallowe'en	59
Come Out, Elves and Fairies	64-65

Songs for Armistice Day
Flag Song	30-31
The Soldier Boy	81
A Soldier True	83
The Star-Spangled Banner	121-123
America	124

Songs for Thanksgiving Day
A Hymn of Thanks	36-37
Gifts of God	37
Thanksgiving Day	51
Praise Ye the Lord	54-55
The Harvest Home	62
Morning Hymn of Praise	93

Songs for Christmas
Christmas	43
Christmas Joy	58
Christmas Hymn	118-119

Songs for New Year's Day
Through the Year	5
Song of the Seasons	18-19
Teach Us to Pray	36-37
Gifts of God	37
Winter Song	70-71
Sing a Song	73

Songs for Lincoln's Birthday
Flag Song	30-31
The Star-Spangled Banner	121-123
America	124

Songs for St. Valentine's Day
The Tiny Little Wood	96-97
My Valentine	114-115

Songs for Washington's Birthday
Flag Song	30-31
A Soldier True	83
America	124

Songs for Easter
The Bird	39
Bluebird, Bluebird	47
A New World	76
Hot Cross-Buns	78
Easter Carol	85
Wonderland	92-93

Songs for Decoration Day
Flag Song	30-31
A Soldier True	83
America	124

Songs for Flag Day
Flag Song	30-31
The Star-Spangled Banner	121-123

Songs for Arbor Day
The Cottonwoods	38
The Bird	39
The Little Path	41

	PAGE
Apple Blossoms	46
May Day	91
The Apple Tree	100-101
Plant a Tree	103

Songs for the Last Day of School
Balloon Song	6
A Merry Comrade	12-13
The Merry-Go-Round	16-17
Playtime Song	28-29
A Hymn of Thanks	36-37
The Little Path	41
Alphabet Song	74-75
Ships	77
A Soldier True	83
Marching Song	98-99

Songs for Autumn
The Harvest Home	62
Summer, Good-by	82
The Apple Tree	100-101

Songs for Winter
Song of the Seasons	18-19
Who's at the Door?	25
The Snow	44-45
Invitations	63
Winter Song	70-71
The Snowbird	71

Songs for Spring
A Merry Comrade	12-13
Song of the Seasons	18-19
The Bird	39
Apple Blossoms	46-47
Bluebird, Bluebird	47
A New World	76
May Day	91
Wonderland	92-93
A Spring Maid	112-113
Spring Song	115

Songs for Summer
The Fairy Piper	7
A-Dancing	15
Fairies	24
The Cottonwoods	38
Hum, Hum, Hum	60
Come Out, Elves and Fairies	64-65

Songs For Morning
Teach Us To Pray	36
The Weather Vane	42
A Morning Prayer	43
Morning Song	55
Sing a Song	73
Morning Hymn of Praise	93
Marching Song	98-99

Songs for Evening
Evening Song	9
A Hymn of Thanks	36-37
The Little Path	41
Honeybee	61
Night Song	108

Marching Songs
The Parade	80
The Soldier Boy	81
A Soldier True	83
Marching Song	98-99

Dance Songs
	PAGE
Through the Year	5
A-Dancing	15
Playtime Song	28-29
Heel and Toe	67

Game Songs
Playtime Song	28-29
The Harvest Home	62
Alphabet Song	74-75

Pantomime Songs
The Cuckoo Clock	10-11
Tick-Tock	20-21
Happy Rosina	26-27
The Parade	80
The Young Musician	86
Baking a Cake	89
The Postilion	106-107

Songs of Out-of Doors
Through the Year	5
Balloon Song	6
The Fairy Piper	7
A Merry Comrade	12-13
The Bird's Song	14-15
A-Dancing	15
Song of the Seasons	18-19
Butterfly	34-35
The Cottonwoods	38
The Bird	39
The Little Path	41
The Weather Vane	42
The Snow	44-45
Apple Blossoms	46-47
Bluebird, Bluebird	47
Questions and Answers	53
Hum, Hum, Hum	60
Honeybee	61
Invitations	63
The Thirsty Flowers	68
Winter Song	70-71
The Snowbird	71
A New World	76
Ships	77
The Echo	79
The Humming Bird	84-85
Wonderland	92-93
The Apple Tree	100-101
Lady Moon	104-105
Katydid	109
Skating	110-111
A Spring Maid	112-113

Songs about Animals
Butterfly	34-35
Hum, Hum, Hum	60
Honeybee	61
Mary Had a Little Lamb	90
Katydid	109

Songs about Birds
The Bird's Song	14-15
The Bird	39
Bluebird, Bluebird	47
The Snowbird	71
The Humming Bird	84-85

Songs about Trees and Flowers
The Cottonwoods	38
Apple Blossoms	46-47
The Thirsty Flowers	68
The Tiny Little Wood	96-97
The Apple Tree	100-101

Songs about Foreign Lands
The Little Eskimo	56-57
The Magic Ball	102
The Little Papoose	117

Fanciful Songs
	PAGE
The Fairy Piper	7
Fairies	24
Who's at the Door?	25
A Dream	50
Fairy Song	52
Come Out, Elves and Fairies	64-65
A Song of Fairies	72
The Echo	79
The Magic Ball	102
Katydid	109

Lullabies
Slumber Song	22-23
Cradle Song	69
Sleep, Baby, Sleep	87
Lullaby	88

Songs in Lighter Vein
The Cuckoo Clock	10-11
The Merry-Go-Round	16-17
Tick-Tock	20-21
The Sad Story of Little Robert	32-33
The Windmill	40
The Weather Vane	42
Hot Pies	48
Little Polly Flinders	49
What Shall I Sing?	65
Hot Cross-Buns	78
Alphabet Song	74-75
Baking a Cake	89
Mary Had a Little Lamb	90
Sing a Song of Sixpence	94-95
Market Day	101
The Postilion	106-107
Katydid	109

Songs of Work
The Cuckoo Clock	10-11
Tick-Tock	20-21
The Windmill	40
The Mill Wheel	45
Hum, Hum, Hum	60
The Harvest Home	62
Baking a Cake	89
The Postilion	106-107

Songs of Service
The Cuckoo Clock	10-11
Tick-Tock	20-21
The Weather Vane	42
The Mill Wheel	45
A Dream	50
The Thirsty Flowers	68
The Soldier Boy	81
A Soldier True	83
The Young Musician	86
The Apple Tree	100-101
Plant a Tree	103

Religious Songs
A Prayer	8-9
Evening Song	9
Teach Us to Pray	36
A Hymn of Thanks	36-37
Gifts of God	37
A Morning Prayer	43
Praise Ye the Lord	54-55
Morning Song	55
Easter Carol	85
Morning Hymn of Praise	93
Christmas Hymn	118-119
God of Mercy	120
America	124

Patriotic Songs
Flag Song	30-31
The Star-Spangled Banner	121-123
America	124

ALPHABETICAL INDEX

		PAGE
A-Dancing	Slovene Folk Song	15
Alphabet Song	Mayhew L. Lake	74-75
America	Henry Carey	124
Apple Blossoms	H. Simon	46-47
Apple Tree, The	Carl Reinecke	100-101
Baking a Cake	Russian Folk Song	89
Balloon Song	Melody by Beethoven	6
Bird, The	German Folk Song used by Brahms	39
Bird's Song	Russian Peasant's Folk Song	14-15
Bluebird, Bluebird	German Folk Song	47
Butterfly	Bohemian Folk Song	34-35
Christmas	Carl Wilhelm	43
Christmas Hymn	Praetorius	118-119
Christmas Joy	C. G. Herring	58
Columbus	C. W. Gluck	116
Come Out, Elves and Fairies	Engelbert Humperdinck	64-65
Cottonwoods, The	Danish Folk Melody	38
Cradle Song	M. Hauser	69
Cuckoo Clock, The	Hebrew Folk Song	10-11
Dream, A	F. A. Boïeldieu	50
Easter Carol	Old German	85
Echo, The	French Game Tune	79
Evening Song	Folk Song	9
Fairies	Christoph Wilibald von Gluck	24
Fairy Piper, The	Melody by Mendelssohn	7
Fairy Song	Old German	52
Flag Song	Moravian Folk Song	30-31
Gifts of God	Johann Sebastian Bach	37
God of Mercy	German Chorale	120
Hallowe'en	J. Offenbach	59
Happy Rosina	French Folk Song	26-27
Harvest Home, The	English Game Song	62
Heel and Toe	Used by Humperdinck	67
Honeybee	German Folk Song	61
Hot Cross-Buns	Old Song	78
Hot Pies		48
Hum, Hum, Hum	German Folk Song	60
Humming Bird, The	Tyrolese Melody	84-85
Hymn of Thanks, A	From Beethoven's Ninth Symphony	36-37
Invitations	Caesar Cui	63
Katydid	Frederick Winthrop	109
Lady Moon	Japanese Song	104-105
Little Eskimo, The	J. Offenbach	56-57
Little Papoose, The	Navajo Indian Melody	117
Little Path, The	A. Maillart	41
Little Polly Flinders		49
Lullaby	French Folk Song	88
Magic Ball, The	Chinese Melody	102

		PAGE
Marching Song	French Folk Song	98-99
Market Day	Bahama Folk Tune	101
Mary Had a Little Lamb	English Folk Song	90
May Day	French Folk Song	91
Merry Comrade, A	J. B. Weckerlin	12-13
Merry-Go-Round, The	Melody by Schumann	16-17
Mill Wheel, The	French Melody	45
Morning Hymn of Praise	Folk Tune	93
Morning Prayer, A	Folk Tune	43
Morning Song		55
My Valentine	J. Offenbach	114-115
New World, A	Old Tune	76
Night Song	Ferdinand Hiller	108
Parade, The	F. A. Boïeldieu	80
Plant a Tree	W. A. Mozart	103
Playtime Song	Old Song	28-29
Postilion, The	William Taubert	106-107
Praise Ye the Lord	Polish Folk Song	54-55
Prayer, A	Melody by Mozart	8-9
Questions and Answers	French Folk Tune	53
Sad Story of Little Robert, The	Russian Folk Song	32-33
Ships	Bohemian Folk Song	77
Sing a Song	W. A. Mozart	73
Sing a Song of Sixpence	J. W. Elliott	94-95
Skating	P. Lacome	110-111
Sleep, Baby, Sleep	Folk Song	87
Slumber Song	Arranged from Carl Spezier	22-23
Snow, The	German Folk Song	44-45
Snowbird, The	Carl Wilhelm	71
Soldier Boy, The	Old English Tune	81
Soldier True, A	Folk Song	83
Song of Fairies, A	Polish Folk Song	72
Song of the Seasons	Bohemian Folk Song	18-19
Spring Maid, A	Holland Folk Tune	112-113
Spring Song	Giuseppe Verdi	115
Star-Spangled Banner, The	John Stafford Smith	121-123
Summer, Good-by	German Folk Song	82
Teach Us to Pray	Gregorian Chant	36
Thanksgiving Day	D. F. E. Auber	51
Thirsty Flowers, The	K. A. Kern	68
Through the Year	Folk Song	5
Tick-Tock	Serbian Folk Song	20-21
Tiny Little Wood, The	French Folk Song	96-97
Weather Vane, The		42
What Shall I Sing?	Adapted from an English Folk Song	66
Who's at the Door?	Breton Melody	25
Windmill, The	French Folk Song	40
Winter Song	Old French Song	70-71
Wonderland	German Folk Song	92-93
Young Musician, The	Old Swabian Folk Song	86